国家汉办/孔子学院总部
Hanban(Confucius Institute Headquarters)

A Cartoon Biography of
Confucius
孔 子 卡 通 传 记 ④
忠 恕 之 道 Doctrine of Loyalty and Forgiveness

青岛出版社
QINGDAO PUBLISHING HOUSE
国家一级出版社
全国百佳图书出版单位

Dear readers and friends interested in learning Chinese,

When you start to learn about the Chinese language and culture at the Confucius Institute and the Confucius Classroom, you must be full of enthusiasm with the expectation for a set of textbooks that will help you not only learn about Chinese language and culture but also satisfy your curiosity about Confucius.

It is hoped that this textbook based upon the animated series 'Confucius' will meet this need.

At the 25th Olympic Games, it was exciting to see Rebollo from Barcelona light the Olympic flame with an arrow. Yet more than 2,500 years ago when a young teacher in China taught his students the "six arts", he already required them to aim their arrows and to hit the target to the rhythm of the music. He was the first man in China who advocated that one should learn with joy, or in his words "those who merely like what they do are not equal to those who delight in what they do". This young teacher was no other than Confucius who later became a great thinker and educator.

His life story from a poor boy to the Eternal Model Teacher is a legend that has inspired many.

No matter which country you come from, no matter whether you are a beginner or have studied Chinese for some time, you are bound to be moved by the stories of Confucius in this textbook. If you come to understand Confucius' ideas of love, uprightness, trust and benevolence for all, it is then a start upon the journey to understand China and Chinese culture. It has been our firm belief that the exchanges between countries are in fact exchanges between individual people and is about communicating heart to heart. In this respect culture is the link by which the peoples exchange, communicate and establish friendship. Confucius said well, "A most valuable use of the rites and protocol is to achieve harmony," and "Virtue is not left to stand alone. He who practises it will have neighbours".

Thank you again for choosing this set of textbooks.

Authors

亲爱的热爱汉语学习的朋友们：

当你们满怀激情和求知的愿望来到孔子学院、孔子课堂，开始汉语言文化学习的时候，你们肯定会希望有一套既能了解中国文化又能学习汉语知识的读物，使你们能以最简便的方式了解到中国的文化，同时解开你们对"孔子"的好奇心。

这部由动画片《孔子》改编的教材，希望能满足你的这个需求。

在25届奥运会上，巴塞罗那选手雷波洛用箭矢点燃了奥运圣火，让人激动不已；而在2500多年前，中国的一位年轻老师教授学生学习"六艺"的时候，就要求学生能踏着音乐的节拍用箭矢射中目标。因此，他成为了中国提出快乐学习的第一人，所谓好之者不如乐之者就是他提出来的。这个年轻的教师就是后来成为伟大思想家、教育家的孔子。

他由一位贫贱少年成长为万世师表的故事，充满了传奇与励志色彩。

无论你来自世界的哪一个国家，无论你是汉语初学者，还是已经入门者，通过这套读物，你将会为《孔子》所讲述的故事所感动；如果你由此理解了孔子思想中关于仁爱、正义、诚信、心怀他人的理念，那将是你了解中国和中国文化的开始。我们一直相信，国与国的交往，其实是人与人的交往，是心与心的沟通。而文化是人们交流沟通、建立友谊的最好纽带。正如孔子所说："礼之用，和为贵"，"德不孤，必有邻"。

再次感谢你选择这套读物。

编者

Contents 目录

01

Si Chi

● 《驷赤》

One late night, all was quiet and the moonlight was clear. Only the sound of carriage wheels rolling on the road could be heard.

It was the carriage of Confucius, the Minister of Justice of the State of Lu. He was heading in the direction of Lord Ji's home.

About an hour ago, the servant of Lord Ji delivered an urgent letter to Confucius and

asked him to go to Ji's mansion to discuss matters of great importance.

When Confucius entered the great hall at Lord Ji's mansion, he saw the three Lords, Lord Ji, Lord Mengsun and Lord Shusun all sitting there with worried looks.

Lord Shusun spoke first, "Amongst my vassals, there is one called Hou Fan. He has killed the governor of the City of Houyi and occupied the city. He is getting ready to give himself a title. You must all help

一天深夜，月光清冷，万籁俱寂，只能听到马车轱辘压过地面、向前滚动的声音。

这是鲁国大司寇孔子的马车，他要前往的地方是季氏大人的家。

就在半个时辰之前，季氏家仆送来一封急信，请孔子立刻前往季府商谈要紧的事。

孔子走进季家大厅，看见季氏、孟孙、叔孙三位大人都坐在屋里，脸上挂着愁容。

叔孙大人率先说："我的家臣里有个叫侯犯的，杀了郈邑宰，占了郈邑城，准备封自个儿为侯呢，大家快帮我出出主意吧。"

me think of something quickly."

Confucius thought for a while and then said,"Most of the city walls nowadays are higher than three meters, so cities have become easy to defend, but difficult to attack. That's why the vassals dare to conspire and rebel. I suggest we demolish these extra city walls to avoid future troubles by other vassals."

After Lord Shusun returned home, he kept thinking back to what Confucius had said. Early next morning, a visitor came to see him.

Lord Shusun recognized that the young man was his vassal Si Chi who was in charge of the craftsmen in the City of Hou. He couldn't help but ask,"Has Hou Fan sent you here to negotiate with me?"

Si chi replied,"I am here only to buy materials, I have no other intentions."

"What is your view of Hou Fan's rebellion?"Lord Shusun asked tentatively.

"I once heard from Master Confucius a poem called Yang Zhi Shui"Si Chi recited calmly,"The water clear and bright runs over pebbles white. Your

孔子思考片刻后说："现在大部分的城墙都超过了一丈，容易守，不容易攻，所以家臣才敢谋反。我建议把多出来的城墙拆掉，才能防止将来其他家臣作乱。"

叔孙大人回家之后，反复想着孔子的话。第二天一早，他家里来了一位客人。

叔孙大人认出前来拜访的年轻人是他的家臣驷赤，在郈邑管理工

匠。他不禁问道："侯犯让你来跟我谈判吗？"

驷赤说："臣只是来国都采购材料，没有其他的意思。"

"侯犯叛乱，你怎么看？"叔孙大人试探地问。

"臣曾经听孔子先生讲过一首诗——《扬之水》。"驷赤平静地念了起来，"扬之水，白石粼粼。我闻有命，不敢以告人。"

word in mind we bear, to tell others we don't dare."

Hearing this, Lord Shusun was confused. He did not know what Si Chi meant.

A few days later, Si Chi bought all the materials he needed and drove back to the City of Houyi.

As soon as he entered the

city, a man with a big beard caught him by the hand, "You have finally returned?"

This bearded person was Fan Hou. His small eyes flickered as he asked, "You have met that old man Shusun, is there any new movement on his side?"

Si Chi rubbed his chin, "Lord Shusun has the backing of the Duke and the three Huans. We must also find someone who can

叔孙大人听得一头雾水，不知道他到底是什么意思。

几天后，驷赤买齐了需要的材料，驾起马车回到郈邑。

刚进城，一个留着大胡子的家伙就猛地抓住了他的手："你回来了？"

那个大胡子正是侯犯，他眨巴着小眼睛问："你去见了叔孙老头儿，他最近有什么动作啊？"

驷赤摸着下巴："叔孙大人背后有国君和三桓支持他，咱们得找个靠山。"

侯犯问："找谁呢？"

support us."

Hou Fan asked,"Who would do that?"

Si Chi replied,"I heard that an envoy from the State of Qi is here, we can talk things over with him."

Hearing this, Hou Fan was very pleased,"I'll tell you a secret. In fact I am already negotiating with that envoy in order to give this city to Qi and in return, they will let me continue to govern here."

Having said that, Hou Fan led Si Chi to the warehouse where several hundred leather armour suits were piled. These were Lord Shusun's past military reserve supplies.

Hou Fan picked up one suit and threw it to Si Chi and said,"This is for you. If you wear this, you will no longer have to be afraid of pikes and swords."

Si Chi's eyes flickered,"There are so many of them. I think that we might as well distribute

驷赤说："听说齐国来了位使者，咱们可以和他谈谈。"

侯犯一听，非常高兴："告诉你一个秘密，其实我正在和那位使者商量把郈邑献给齐国，他们承诺还让我来管理。"

说着，他把驷赤拉到仓库，那儿堆放着几百件青色的皮甲，是叔孙大人过去储存的军备物资。

侯犯随手拿起一件扔给驷赤，说："送你一件。穿上它，刀枪都不怕！"

驷赤眨眨眼："这么多皮甲？不如咱们分发给老百姓吧，到时也好帮着一块儿抵抗叔孙大人啊。"

侯犯哈哈大笑："有道理！"

them to the common people in the city so that they could help resist Lord Shusun's army when needed."

Hou Fan laughed,

"Rightly so."

Upon Hou Fan's approval, Si Chi gathered the people in the city and gave everyone a suit of leather armour.

Looking at one another, everyone seemed puzzled,

"What is this for?"

Si Chi said to them quietly, "Hou Fan is going to give our city away to the State of Qi and make us citizens of Qi. Are you going to accept that?"

"What? There's no way we are going to accept that!"The people started to shout one after another.

得到侯犯的同意后，驷赤把城里的老百姓召集起来，一人发了一件皮甲。

老百姓们你看我，我看你，都不明白："发这个给我们干什么？"

驷赤悄悄地对他们说："侯犯要把郈邑献给齐国，让咱们变成齐国人。你们愿意吗？"

"什么？我们才不愿意呢！"大伙儿纷纷嚷了起来。

"那就跟我走吧！"驷赤一声令下，郈邑的百姓们穿上皮甲，拿起棍棒，浩浩荡荡地冲进了郈邑宰府。

"Then come with me!"At Si Chi's command, the people in the City of Houyi all donned the suits of leather armour, took up makeshift weapons and stormed Hou Fan's mansion.

There was a storeroom in the backyard of the city governor's mansion. Inside the storeroom were lines of shelves where all the household registers were kept. Standing in front of the shelves, Hou Fan narrowed his eyes and looked at the dust covered scrolls.

"In a few days'time, every file and every name will have a stamp bearing the mark of the State of Qi!"A smile crept on his face. "From then on, I won't need to worry about money or titles anymore."

Just as Hou Fan was indulging in his fanciful dreams, suddenly he heard the door was kicked open with a crash. He turned around and saw Si Chi standing at the entrance with many other people from the city, all carrying burning torches and had angry looks

郈邑宰府后院里有一间保管室，成排的木架上存放着城里所有老百姓的户籍资料。侯犯站在木架前，眯起眼睛看着那些积满灰尘的简册。

"过几天，这里的每一个简册、每一个名字，都将打上齐国的符号！"他的脸上不禁浮现出一丝微笑，"到那时，我就不愁荣华富贵了。"

他正沉浸在美妙的遐想中，忽然听到门被人踢开的声音，回头一看，只见驷赤和一群拿着火把的老百姓站在门口，个个脸上都挂着怒色。

侯犯心虚地往后退了退："你们想干吗？"

驷赤沉着地说："这话应当问你自己！"

on their faces.

Hou Fan stepped back and said nervously, "What do you think you are doing?"

Si Chi replied sternly, "This should be the question for you."

Hou Fan suddenly realised what was happening. He pointed at Si Chi and cursed, "So you only pretended to help me, didn't you? You traitor!"

People all jeered at him, "Ha haha, we all know who the real traitor is here."

"Go! "Si Chi waved his hand coldly, "We spare your life, but you never come back to the State of Lu again!"

In the midst of everyone's shouts, Hou Fan hurriedly fled via the backdoor without even packing his possessions.

A few days later, Lord Shusun received the news and

　　侯犯一下子明白过来，指着驷赤大骂起来："原来你一直是假装帮我的，对吗？你这个叛徒！"

　　老百姓们冷笑起来："哈哈哈，不知道到底谁是叛徒！"

　　"走吧！"驷赤冷冷地把手一挥，"放你一条生路，你以后不要再回鲁国了！"

　　在老百姓的呐喊声中，侯犯连包裹都来不及收拾，就仓皇地从后门逃走了。

　　几天后，叔孙大人得知了这个消息，火速赶到郈邑城，激动地对驷赤说："你既让老百姓避免了战乱，又把叛臣侯犯赶跑了。谢谢你！"

rushed to the City of Hou. He said to Si Chi emotionally,"You have managed to drive out the rebel and spared the city from suffering an all out war. Thank you very much!"

Si Chi smiled,"It is the Lord Minister of Justice that you should really thank. I once learned from him a poem titled Yang Zhi Shui:'The torrents of the river are flow endlessly, and the white pebbles at the bottom of the river looked clear and bright. When I heard that there is a secret order, I wouldn't dare to tell anyone else.'It is this poem that has taught me to be a gentleman loyal to the State."

驷赤微微一笑："其实你要感谢的是司寇大人。我曾经向他学过一首《扬之水》：'激扬的河水不断流淌，水底的白石更显晶莹。当我听说将有机密的命令，怎么也不敢告诉别人。'正是这首诗教会我要做一个忠于国家的君子。"

02 Seeking a Favour
·《求情》

After Lord Shusun regained the City of Houyi, Duke Ding of Lu especially held a banquet for him.

Almost everyone present at the banquet was congratulating Lord Shusun, from the Duke to all the civil and military officials. Lord Shusun was all smiles toasting and thanking everyone.

There was only one person in the spacious palace hall

who looked very serious with his brows knitted. That was Confucius.

The Duke saw this and asked him, "Why are you not drinking?"

Confucius replied,"I think that it is not yet the time to drink and celebrate. We have just regained the City of Houyi. Why don't we take this opportunity to demolish the city walls of all the feudum cities?"

Upon hearing this, everyone put down his cup and looked at Lords Ji, Lord Shusun and Lord Mengsun.

叔孙大人收复郈邑之后，鲁定公专门为他办了一个宴会。

在宴会上，上至鲁定公，下到文武百官，无不高声恭贺。叔孙大人乐呵呵地举杯道谢。

偌大的宫殿里，只有一个人紧锁眉头，满面严肃。这个人就是孔子。

鲁定公看到了，问他："你怎么不喝酒呀？"

孔子说："臣认为，现在还不到喝酒庆祝的时候。如今郈邑刚刚收复，我们为何不趁这个机会拆掉各个封邑的城墙呢？"

大家听了，都放下酒杯，把目光投向了在座的季氏、叔孙氏和孟孙氏。

Lord Shusun thought for a moment and expressed his agreement first,"It is really a problem when vassals rebel. I certainly don't want to go through that again. Therefore, I agree with the proposal by the Minister of Justice."

Lord Ji also thought for a moment and commented, "I have a vassal by the name of Gongshan Buniu. He is governing the City of Fei for me, but often ignores my commands. It will be good to teach him a lesson by taking down the city walls."

The last of the three Huans Lord Mengsun appeared to be hesitant and didn't speak. Nobody could guess whether he agreed or disagreed with the proposal.

Duke Ding of Lu asked him,"Lord Mengsun, you were a student of the Minister of Justice. Regarding his proposal, you would not have any objections I presume?"

"No objection, of course not!" Lord Mengsun nodded repeatedly, but his eyes were fixed on the ground with perspiration on his forehead.

叔孙大人想了想，第一个表示同意："家臣作乱是件麻烦事，我可不想再经历一次了。我同意大司寇的提议。"

季氏大人想了想，也说："我有个家臣叫公山不狃。他替我管理费邑，也老不听命令，拆掉城墙，教训他一下也好。"

三桓中的最后一位孟孙大人此时却支支吾吾，半天不说话，叫人猜不透他是同意，还是不同意。

鲁定公问他："孟孙大人，你过去是司寇大人的学生，对他的提议，应该不会反对吧？"

"不反对，不反对！"孟孙大人连连点头，可眼睛却盯着地板，额头微微渗出了冷汗。

After he returned home, he said to his younger brother Nangong,"Brother, we have a problem. Please go and ask for help from the Minister of Justice."

Nangong was troubled,"The Master was right to suggest this. Moreover, he may not listen to me anyway."

"You have married his niece and he trusts you very much. So please go and at least have a try."This was the first time that Lord Mengsun begged his

younger brother for help.

Nangong didn't want to disappoint his elder brother, so in the end he could only agree.

The next day, two visitors came to Confucius'home -Nangong and his wife Wujia.

Seeing the expression on Nangong's face, Confucius guessed the reason for his visit and asked, "Are you here on behalf of your elder brother?"

回去以后，孟孙氏对弟弟南宫说："弟弟呀，咱们有麻烦了。你去向大司寇求求情吧。"

南宫感到很为难："可是先生说得很有道理。再说，我的话他不一定会听。"

"你娶了先生的侄女，他很信任你，去试试吧！"这是孟孙大人头一次恳求弟弟。

南宫不想看到哥哥这么难过，只好答应了。

第二天，孔子家里来了两位客人——南宫与他的夫人无加。

看着南宫的表情，孔子已经料到了，问："你是不是帮你哥哥求情来了？"

Nangong nodded,"My elder brother said that cities within his fiefdom are close to the border with the State of Qi. If the walls are demolished, the cities would be in great danger." Looking at Nangong, Confucius said with a serious tone,"The cause of the chaos in the State of Lu is that vassals do not obey their lords, and lords do not obey their Duke. Therefore, the only solution to bring about stability to the State is to take down the city walls. You brothers were my students, so you should understand this better than anyone else."

Nangong felt a bit ashamed to hear this,"I am sorry. I will go back and persuade him to support you, Master."

南宫点点头："我哥哥说，他的封邑靠近齐国边境，若是拆了城墙，就危险了。"

孔子看着南宫，严肃地说："鲁国混乱的原因就在于家臣不听大夫的话，大夫又不听国君的话，所以拆掉城墙，才能够真正稳定鲁国。你们兄弟二人都是我的学生，更应该明白事理啊。"

南宫听了十分惭愧："对不起，学生这就回去劝他支持先生！"

03 Rebellion
《叛乱》

The three most powerful aristocrats in the State of Lu all agreed to take down the walls of their feudum cities. Zilu was put in charge of the task, which was termed as the "Dismantling of the Three Citadels".

At Zilu's command, the Lu troops first demolished the high walls of the City of Houyi, and then they marched towards the City of Feiyi.

The person who governed that city was Gongshan Buniu, a vassal of the Lord Ji. He was a very cunning person.

He had heard early in the morning that Zilu and the army were coming to demolish his city walls, so he led his soldiers and they sneaked to the capital where the defence was then very relaxed. There he planned to capture Duke Ding of Lu and Lord Ji.

Soon Gongshan Buniu and his army surrounded the Palace. The air was filled with the sound of clashing weapons, chaotic footsteps and the cracklings of the fires burning.

鲁国的三个大贵族终于都同意拆除自己的封邑城墙了。这个行动被命名为"堕三都",由子路负责。

子路率领大批鲁国将士,首先拆除了郈邑的高墙,接着浩浩荡荡地朝着费邑开去。

管理费邑的人名叫公山不狃,是季氏大人的家臣。他是个非常狡猾的家伙。

他一早就听说子路带着军队来费邑拆城墙,于是悄悄带兵跑到了守卫空虚的国都,准备捉拿鲁定公和季氏大人。

很快,公山不狃的军队就包围了王宫。空气里传来兵器的碰撞声、杂乱的脚步声,还有火焰燃烧时发出的噼里啪啦的声音。

Duke Ding of Lu hid in the backyard with a few of his guards. He was trembling with fright and thought to himself: My God, can I survive this?

As his thoughts were roaming wildly, a chariot charged out and thundered towards them. The people on the chariot used their swords to fend off the pikes of the soldiers from the City of Feiyi and quickly reached Duke Ding of Lu.

They turned out to be Confucius and his students Yan Hui and Zigong. They helped Duke Ding into the chariot and then quickly drove off into the darkness and towards the mansion of Lord Ji.

In the courtyard of Lord Ji's mansion, there was a high platform which was wide at the base and narrow at the top, just like a pyramid. Confucius helped Duke Ding of Lu as they slowly walked up to the top where Lord Ji was already waiting. With shields in their hands, Lord Ji's soldiers stood in a circle around Duke Ding of Lu and Lord Ji to protect them.

鲁定公和几名卫兵躲在后院里，吓得浑身发抖。他心想："天啊，寡人能逃过这一劫吗？"

就在他胡思乱想之际，一辆马车如闪电般冲了出来。车上的人挥舞着宝剑，挡开费邑将士的长戈，来到鲁定公面前。

原来是孔子和他的学生——颜回、子贡。他们将

鲁定公扶上车，疾驰的马车在黑夜中疾速奔向季氏大人的宅邸。

季府的大院里有一座高台，下宽上窄，就像一座塔。孔子扶着鲁定公慢慢走上去，季氏大人已经在那高高的台顶等候。季府士兵拿着盾牌，站成一圈，把他们保护起来。

Gongshan Buniu and his soldiers soon arrived. They flocked to climb the steps that led to the top of the platform.

Suddenly Lord Ji's soldiers moved away their shields, boulders and logs were rolling down the steps and knocked the rebel troops back to the ground.

"So they are well prepared!" said Gongshan Buniu angrily. "Archers, shoot!"

In the light of the fires, waves of arrows flew past the boulders and shields and fell at the feet of Confucius and his companions.

Duke Ding was trembling, "This is frightening. Shall we seek peace from them?"

Confucius said sternly, "How could a Monarch seek peace from his subordinates? Please trust me!"

不消片刻，公山不狃的追兵就赶到了。他们争先恐后地沿着台阶往上爬。

忽然，季府士兵拿开了手里的盾牌，只见一块块巨大的石头和圆木咕噜咕噜地往下滚去，把叛军将士们撞回了地面。

"原来他们早有准备了！"公山不狃愤愤地骂道，"来人，放箭！"

火光中，黑压压的箭飞上高台，越过盾牌与石头，落在孔子他们的脚边。

鲁定公禁不住颤抖起来："太可怕了！我们求和吧？"

孔子严肃地说："国君岂能向下人求和？请相信臣！"

He stood up, and looked at Yan Hui. Yan Hui immediately understood and handed him a bow and arrow.

The bow didn't have any special features, but the arrow had a hole in its head and its shaft was thin and smooth. Once the arrow was shot out, it would make a loud high pitch sound in the air. It was a whistling arrow.

In the darkness, two large groups of soldiers heard the whistling arrow. The leader who commanded these soldiers drew out his sword and said loudly, "The Lord Minister of Justice has now given us the signal. Follow me to surround the high platform and attack the rebels!"

The two groups of soldiers quickly charged forward and surrounded the army of Gongshan Buniu.

他站起来，向颜回递了一个眼色。颜回立刻交给他一副弓箭。

这把弓并没有什么特别之处，但那支箭的箭头上却穿了一个孔，箭身也特别纤细流畅。一经出去，它就在空中发出"呜呜"的鸣声。原来，这是一支响箭。

黑暗中，有两队士兵听到了箭响。带队的司马拔出宝剑，大声说："司寇大人发信号了。大家跟我去包抄高台，袭击叛军！"

两列队伍整齐、迅速地向前冲去，把公山不狃的军队团团围住。

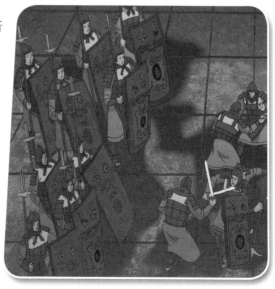

"It's a trap!"Gongshan Buniu turned round his chariot and fled. His soldiers threw down their weapons and dispersed in all directions.

Thus, the rebels were defeated.

At the top of the high platform, Duke Ding and Lord Ji both sighed with relief, feeling great after a narrow escape from death.

Duke Ding said earnestly,"Lord Minister of Justice, you have once again saved the State of Lu."

"有圈套！"公山不狃驾起马车掉头就跑，他的士兵们全都扔下兵器，一哄而散了。

就这样，叛军被打败了。

在高高的台顶上，鲁定公和季氏大人长长地松了一口气，真有一种死里逃生的感觉。

鲁定公诚恳地说："司寇大人，您又一次挽救了鲁国。"

04

A Spy

《奸细》

After the Cities of Houyi and Fei yi were pacified, there was only one city left, the City of Chengyi that belonged to Lord Mengsun.

Under the moonlight, all was quiet at Lord Mengsun's mansion. The long and dark corridors were only dimly lit by the few torches placed on the walls. Two people walked along, the one in front was Lord Mengsun's vassal Gonglian Chufu, the one behind had his face covered and was holding a wooden cage in his arms.

They entered a room and saw that Lord Mengsun was sitting by the brazier, warming himself.

The first word from Gonglian Chufu was, "My Lord, you must not be foolish. You cannot allow your city walls to be taken down!"

Lord Mengsun sighed helplessly, "I don't want that either, but it is hard to back down now."

Gonglian Chufu moved forward and said in a low voice, "There is a way. I shall return and resist quietly. You just need to pretend that you don't know anything about it."

平定了郈邑和费邑这两座城以后，就只剩下孟孙大人的郕邑了。

月光下，孟孙氏的大宅十分安静，走廊幽暗而狭长，靠着几根插在墙上的火把勉强照出方向。有两个人一前一后地走过来，前一个是孟孙氏的家臣公敛处父，后面跟着一个抱着一只木头笼子的蒙面人。

他们走进屋子，看见孟孙大人正坐在火盆旁边取暖。

公敛处父第一句话就说："大人好糊涂，您的郕邑城墙不能拆啊！"

孟孙大人很无奈："我也不想，可现在已经骑虎难下了。"

公敛处父上前两步，压低嗓门说："有一个办法，我回去悄悄安排抵抗，您这头假装不知道就是了。

"Are you sure it will work?" Lord Mengsun became interested.

"I have two magic treasures."

Gonglian Chufu lifted the cloth that covered the wooden cage, inside was a strange and ugly bird. The man beside him who had his face covered also removed the cloth.

"One is this bird which we can use to exchange messages; the other is Gongbo Liao who will help us in secret." After saying that, Gonglian Chufu laughed smugly.

"Gongbo Liao?" Lord

Mengsun was scrutinizing the man who had just uncovered his thin angular face. "Who are you, and how can you help me?"

Gongbo Liao chuckled, "I work under Lord Zilu, so I can provide you with inside information."

Lord Mengsun was both shocked and pleased.

He immediately asked the two to sit down and they talked through the whole night. It was not until dawn was breaking over the eastern skies did he finally bid them to leave.

"有把握吗？"孟孙大人不由得动了心。

"我有两个法宝。"

公敛处父一把撩起盖住那只木笼子的布，只见里边有一只长相丑陋的怪鸟。而他身边的蒙面人也拉下了面巾。

"一靠这只鸟传递情报，二靠公伯僚暗中相助！"公敛处父说完，得意地笑了起来。

"公伯僚？"孟孙大人仔细地打量那个尖嘴猴腮的蒙面人，"你是什么人？你要如何助我呢？"

公伯僚嘿嘿一笑："小的在子路大人手底下行事，我可以把内部的情报都传出来。"

孟孙大人又惊又喜，连忙邀请两人坐下，一夜长谈，直到东方出现了一抹鱼肚白，才让他们离开。

"Now let's see how you are going to demolish the walls of my City of Chengyi?" Tired but assured, Lord Mengsun finally went to sleep.

A few days later, Zilu and his troop arrived at the City of Chengyi. They found the city gate was tightly shut and the city walls were several times higher than those of the City of Houyi and City of Feiyi.

Zilu blinked, but before he could recover from his surprise, a line of archers suddenly appeared on the rampart with arrows on their bows.

The next moment, arrows were showering down along with stones and logs.

Zilu ordered his army to withdraw and set up camp in the distance.

It was a freezing cold night. There were very few trees around and the shallow streams were covered in ice and snow. Sitting in the tents, they felt as if they were sitting in an icehouse.

Zilu was giving instructions to his troops. "We shall launch a surprise attack on the City of Chengyi tonight. Use ropes to climb the high wall and then open the city gates."

"这下，看你们怎么拆我的郈邑！"在这个让人疲惫而又颇感欣慰的清晨，孟孙大人舒舒坦坦地睡着了。

几天之后，子路的部队来到郈邑，发现城门紧紧关闭着，其城墙比郈邑和费邑的城墙高出好几倍。

子路眨眨眼，没等回过神来，城墙上忽然出现了一排弓箭手，齐齐地拉弓放箭。

一时间，箭如急雨，石头和原木也纷纷滚下。

子路号令将士们退下，在远处扎起了军营。

那是个寒冷的夜晚，树木稀疏，溪涧浅落，到处都是冰和雪。他们坐在营帐中，就好像坐在冰窖里。

子路正在向他的手下布置任务："今晚突袭郈邑，用绳子爬过高墙，打开城门。"

Hearing this, his subordinate generals were all impetuous for the battle and filled with confidence. Only the person sitting in the corner was silent with his head lowered and a smile on his face. That person was Gongbo Liao.

When nobody was looking, he sneaked out of the tent and to a place with no one in sight. He took out the strange bird that Gonglian Chufu had given him.

The freezing wind was blowing causing Gongbo Liao to shiver. He attached a small

and thin bamboo tube to the leg of the bird. Inside the bamboo was the information about the surprise attack that night.

The strange bird crowed and flew into the sky, then headed towards the high wall of the City of Chengyi.

In the middle of the night, Zilu's attack troop marched soundlessly in the dark and soon reached the foot of the city walls. Scores of soldiers threw out the hooked ropes and caught the battlements.

　　副将们听了，个个摩拳擦掌，信心十足，只有坐在角落里的那个人低着脑袋，赔着笑，一声不吭。这人正是公伯僚。

　　他趁别人不注意，鬼鬼祟祟地摸到营帐外面无人的地方，抱出了公敛处父给他的怪鸟。

　　寒风吹来，公伯僚不禁打了个哆嗦。他在鸟的腿上绑了一支细小的竹筒，里面装上了今夜突袭的情报。

　　怪鸟嘎嘎叫着，蹿上高空，朝郕邑高大的城墙飞去。

　　子夜时分，子路的突袭队伍在黑暗中无声地前进。他们来到城墙根后，数十个士兵朝上扔出绳子，钩住了城垛。

While the soldiers were climbing up the walls one after another, there appeared on the top of the wall a line of torches. The soldiers from the City of Chengyi emerged like ghosts armed with arrows and bows. It was obvious that they have been waiting for this moment.

Zilu was boiling with rage, and he was about to charge in his chariot when his deputy general caught the bridle and said to him,"My Lord, we shouldn't force the attack like this. Let's ask for help from the capital."

This calmed Zilu down and he ordered his troop to pull back.

When his troops were retreating, Gongbo Liao turned around and cast a glance at the high walls. His glance met with that of Gonglian Chufu's and they nodded knowingly at each other.

就在他们接二连三地往上爬时，墙上忽然亮起一排火把，郈邑士兵像幽灵一样出现了，他们手持弓箭，看样子已经等候多时。

子路气得怒发冲天，驾起马车就要往前冲。他的副将一把抓住马辔头，说："大人，不能强攻，咱们赶紧向国都求救吧！"

子路这才恢复了冷静，号令大伙儿撤退。

在跟着大部队向回跑的那一刻，公伯僚回头朝着高高的城墙看了一眼，正好与公敛处父的目光相对。两个人彼此心照不宣地点了点头。

05 To Lead Personally

《亲征》

"Bang!" An urgent letter written on a piece of silk fell heavily on the table. This was the military report sent by Zilu to Confucius.

Zigong, Yan Hui and Nangong all looked at Confucius with a slight tinge of fright as they had never seen him so angry before.

"Zilu says that his troops have suffered heavy losses and they are unable to take the City of Chengyi." Said Confucius,"That Gonglian Chufu even dares to disobey the orders of the Duke".

Nangong lowered his head,"My elder brother told me that Gonglian Chufu had agreed to take down the city walls. How could this be happening?"

"There is something fishy about this." Confucius thought for a moment and walked out of the house. "I am going to discuss this with the Duke."

He went straight to the Palace and requested a meeting with the Duke.

Duke Ding came out of his warm bed and yawned,"What is happening? Is there anything urgent?"

"啪！"一张薄绢写成的急信被重重地拍在几案上，这是子路给孔子写来的军报。

子贡、颜回和南宫有点儿害怕地看着孔子，他们从来没有见过老师这么生气。

"子路说郈邑攻不下来，部队伤亡惨重。"孔子说，"那个公敛处父竟然敢违抗国君的命令！"

南宫低下头："我哥哥告诉我，公敛处父已经同意拆城了。怎么会这样呢？"

"这事有点儿蹊跷。"孔子想了一下，朝着屋外走去，"我去和国君谈谈。"

他径直来到王宫，求见国君。

鲁定公从暖和的被窝里钻出来，打着呵欠问："怎么了？有急事吗？"

Confucius said in a serious tone, "Your Grace, I request that you personally lead an expedition against the City of Chengyi."

These words startled the Duke and he suddenly woke up completely,"What?"

Thus Confucius told the Duke in details about what was in the report sent in by Zilu. Having heard this, the Duke remained silent for a long time. He then spoke with a firm resolution in his eyes, "I will listen to you this time, my Minister of Justice." A few days later, Duke Ding and Confucius set off towards the City of Chengyi together.

The time of the year was the coldest period of winter with heavy snow. It was so cold that even the water flowing out of a cup would turn into ice instantly. While he was sitting in the carriage and watching the banners flying overhead, Duke Ding's heart had already gone back to his beautiful and grand palace.

Suddenly the carriages stopped, the high and solid walls of the City of Cheng were not far in front of them.

Zilu drove his chariot to the front and started to shout,"Gonglian Chufu, both the Duke and the Minister of Justice are here. Lay down your arms now!"

孔子严肃地说："国君，请您亲自出征郈邑吧！"

这话把鲁定公吓得睡意一下子全没了："什么？"

于是，孔子把子路汇报的情况仔仔细细地跟鲁定公说了。鲁定公听罢，半天没说话。当他再度开口时，目光变得异常坚定："这回我听您的，大司寇。"

几日之后，鲁定公和孔子一同朝着郈邑出发了。

这是大雪纷飞的数九寒天，杯子里的水滴出来都会在瞬间结成冰。鲁定公坐在马车上，看着旗帜在头顶飘扬，心思早已飞回自己华美的宫殿。

忽然车队停了下来，高大坚固的郈邑就在眼前。

子路驾车来到最前方，冲着城墙高喊："公敛处父，国君和大司寇都来了，还不放下武器！"

The soldiers standing at the battlements looked at one another and became panic.

One braver soldier asked Gonglian Chufu, "My Lord, even the Duke is here, perhaps we should surrender?"

Gonglian Chufu glared at him, "I only listen to Lord Mengsun. Archers, shoot!"

Hundred of arrows flew over like the venomous insect stings and struck many of Zilu's soldiers and forced them to retreat to a safe spot. Again, they had to abandon their attempt to attack.

When night came, the wind became stronger and produced a brisk sound when blowing on the thin tent. This was accompanied by the sad whining of horses and every now and then the howling of wolves. Duke Ding wrapped himself up in a thick fox fur coat and sat next to the brazier, but he was still shivering with cold and his teeth were chattering.

The journey was rough and the Duke neither ate well nor slept well. He had never suffered like this before, so he decided to return to the capital the following day.

城垛上的士兵们你看我，我看你，都惊慌起来。

其中有个胆大的问公敛处父："大人，连国君都来了，我们是不是该投降啊？"

公敛处父一瞪眼："我只听孟孙大人的，给我放箭！"

几百支又粗又大的箭像毒虫一样飞来，纷纷扎入子路部队的士兵身上。大家不得不又退回到安全地带，放弃了进攻。

到了晚上，风刮得更厉害了，薄薄的帐篷发出"扑哧扑哧"的声音，帐外不时传来凄凉的马嘶和悠长的狼嚎。鲁定公裹着厚厚的狐皮大衣，靠在火炉旁，仍冷得牙齿打架。

这一路奔波，鲁定公吃不好，睡不香。他哪里受过这样的苦，于是决定第二天就回去。

When Confucius learned of this, he was very surprised, "Your Grace, this is the last city. Once its walls are down, the authority of Your Grace will be fully restored and there will be long term peace and stability in the State."

Duke Ding shook his head, "Although my court doesn't have much authority, we don't need to worry too much about this. I am already used to it anyway."

The following day, Duke Ding of Lu insisted on leaving. So the half year long endeavour of "Dismantling of the Three Citadels" ended in failure.

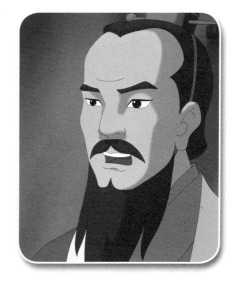

孔子听了，非常惊讶："国君，这是最后一座城了，拆了它，就能恢复公室的权力，国家就能太平安定了。"

鲁定公摇摇头："虽然公室没什么权力，但也不用操这么多心呀。寡人已经习惯了。"

第二天，鲁定公坚持要走。历时半年的"堕三都"行动就这样失败了。

06 Bewitching Scent
《迷香》

One day, Duke Jing of the State of Qi as usual called for a meeting of his ministers in his palace. There they drank wine as they discussed the state affairs.

One minister said worriedly, "The State of Lu has given an important post to Confucius. If this goes on, the State of Lu will become stronger."

Duke Jing put down his cup unhappily and said,"This also worries me. Do you have any good ideas?"

General Li Mi who had fought against Confucius in Jiagu stepped out and said, "I hear that Lord Ji of the State of Lu is very fond of watching dances. Why don't we give him eighty skilful dancing girls and through them turn him against Confucius?"

Saying this, Li Mi waved his hand. From the rear of the room came a young girl wearing a golden mask and a pair of wooden sandals.

一天，齐景公像往常一样召来所有的大臣，一边喝酒，一边商量国家大事。

有个大臣担心地提到："现在鲁国很重用那个孔子。如此下去，鲁国一定会强盛起来呀。"

齐景公不高兴地放下酒杯，说："这件事我也很担忧，你们有什么妙计吗？"

在夹谷与孔子交过手的大将军犁弥站出来说："臣听说鲁国的季氏大人喜欢观看舞蹈，咱们不如送八十名擅长跳舞的姑娘给他，以此挑拨他和孔子的关系，怎么样？"

说着，犁弥一挥手，后头走上来一名脚穿木屐、头戴黄金面具的年轻女孩。

A group of attendants brought over seven shiny and translucent jade plates and placed them on the floor. The girl extended her pale foot and touched the edge of a plate lightly with the tip of her toe. With a twist of her waist, she started to dance gracefully.

The ministers and generals saw her dance and they were all transfixed with their mouth wide open. Yet, Duke Jing just smiled with satisfaction, he knew now that this plan would definitely succeed.

Not long after that, at the hotel outside the south gate of the capital of the State of Lu, a large group of visitors from the State of Qi arrived. They brought with them a hundred and twenty majestic white horses with patterns painted on their bodies and eighty beautiful girls dressed in long red robe who were all adept at dancing and singing. They used the hotel as a staging venue and put on performances for the people of Lu every day.

This news travelled through the State like wildfire and soon everyone in the State of Lu had heard about it. Every day crowds of people from Lu would come to watch the performances.

一队侍从将七个晶莹透亮的玉盘搁在地上。只见那女孩伸出洁白的足尖，轻点盘子边缘，腰身一扭，就跳起柔美的舞来。

在场的文武大臣们看了，都惊叹得合不上嘴。然而，齐景公却满意地笑了，他知道这条计谋一定会成功。

不久之后，鲁国都城南门外的客栈来了一大群齐国客人。他们带

来了一百二十匹身上画着花纹的白色骏马和八十名身穿红色长裙、能歌善舞的美丽女孩，并在客栈里摆开舞台，日日为鲁国人演出。

这消息一传十，十传百，很快鲁国上下都知道了，每天都有大量的鲁国人前来观看歌舞。

The young girl wearing the mask was the most popular performer. Her best act was dancing on the seven jade plates in her wooden sandals accompanied with the dance music called "Rong Ji". Every time when it was her turn to dance, in the lingering incense smoke, the half drunk audience would all cheer loudly, clap their hands with vigour and constantly shout out their approval. They also gave her a nickname - the Rong Ji Dancing Girl.

One day, a magnificent carriage arrived outside the hotel

and a proud looking man came out. It was no other than Lord Ji himself who had come to watch the performance of the female dancers from the State of Qi.

In a short while, the Rong Ji Dancing Girl appeared on the platform.

Accompanied by the dance music, she started to swirl quickly. Her long sleeves flying around her body, just like long, thin colourful clouds.

Lord Ji was completely intoxicated and was even nodding and humming along with the music.

那名戴着面具的年轻女孩最受欢迎。她的拿手好戏是穿着木屐、踩在七个玉盘上跳舞，伴奏的曲子叫做《容玑》。每次轮到她表演的时候，底下的观众们往往已经喝得半醉。在袅袅香烟中，大家无不高声欢呼，大力鼓掌，连连叫好。他们还为她取了一个名字——容玑舞女。

这天，客栈外来了一辆华贵的马车，从车上走下一位高傲的客人。他正是前来观赏齐国女乐的季氏大人。

不一会儿，容玑舞女上场了。

在舞曲的伴奏下，她飞快地旋转起来，长长的袖子围绕身体飞扬，就像细细的彩云。

季氏大人深深地陶醉了，甚至摇头晃脑地跟着唱了起来。

After the performance ended, the Rong Ji Dancing Girl took off her mask and gave Lord Ji a quick smile,"My Lord, if you take me into the city, I am willing to dance for you every day and night."

Lord Ji's carriage went back towards the capital along the route it had come. Suddenly the two horses whinnied and stood up on their hind legs as they came to a halt. The voice of Confucius came from outside the carriage.

"Did my Lord forget that the suburb ceremony for the State of Lu is to be held today?"Confucius'tone sounded stern.

Lord Ji lifted the curtain and Confucius saw a beautiful girl clinging closely to Lord Ji with a mask in her hand. He immediately realised that she was the Rong Ji Dancing Girl from the State of Qi.

"I know that, you go ahead first." With that Lord Ji put down the curtain.

Standing there and watching the carriage disappearing behind the city gate, Confucius shook his head and said sadly,"I had hoped to build the State of Lu as a peaceful world for everyone, but when I look at Lord Ji and the Duke, I find my ideals are more and more difficult to realize."

表演结束后，容玑舞女取下面具，对着季氏大人浅浅一笑："大人，如果您带我进城的话，我愿意日夜为您起舞。"

季氏大人的马车沿着来时的路朝国都跑去。忽然，两匹马扬起前蹄，嘶嘶鸣叫着停了下来。车厢外传来孔子的声音。

"今天是鲁国郊祭的日子，大人忘了吗？"他的语气有点儿严厉。

季氏大人掀开帘子，孔子看见有个美丽的女孩紧紧靠在他身边，手中拿着一个面具。孔子立刻知道，这就是齐国来的容玑舞女。

"我知道了，你先去吧。"季氏大人放下了帘子。

孔子站在原地，看着马车消失在城门后，沉痛地摇摇头说："我曾希望把鲁国建设成一个人人安乐的世界，可看到季氏大人和国君的样子，我觉得越来越难了。"

His student Yan Hui was standing beside him: He thought for a moment and said, "The world is very big, Master. You can consider leaving the State of Lu and go to a state that really appreciates your ideals."

Confucius was startled at this idea, but his interest seemed to be kindled. He lowered his eye lids and said, "Let us wait for a while. We shall first see how today's suburb ceremony goes."

"Suburb ceremony?" Yan Hui and other students looked at each other, very puzzled.

站在他身旁的学生颜回想了想，说："天下很大，先生可以考虑离开鲁国，到一个真正认同先生的理想的国家去。"

孔子一愣，仿佛被这个想法点燃了。随即，他低下眼皮说："再等等，看今天郊祭后会怎样。"

"郊祭？"颜回和师兄弟们对望了一眼，都是一头雾水。

07

Leaving the State of Lu
●《去鲁》

The light breeze was blowing through the fields. In the middle of the fields, there were huge torches made from bunches of rice straws. In front of those torches was a bronze table, upon which there was a piece of roasted beef.

The civil and military officials of the State of Lu stood in a long line, waiting quietly.

An official in charge of protocols appeared holding a broom. He walked slowly forward and presented the bloom to Duke Ding of Lu with both of his hands.

The Duke swept a few times clumsily and the dust stirred up nearly went into his mouth. He put down the bloom and declared that the suburb ceremony to Heaven would now formally begin.

The suburb ceremony to Heaven referred to the sacrificial ceremonies held in the suburbs. It was one of the grandest ceremonies for a state since the beginning of the Zhou Dynasty. After the suburb ceremony had ended, the roast beef (also referred to as Fan Zu) on the bronze table would be distributed to the civil and military officials to express that the state held them in high regard.

微风轻拂的田野中，竖起了一支支用稻草捆成的巨型火把。前方有一个青铜铸成的台子，上面放着一块烤熟的牛肉。

鲁国的文武百官排成长列，在静静地等待着。

一名礼官捧着一把扫帚出现了，他一步一步地走上前来，双手将扫帚交给鲁定公。

鲁定公笨拙地用扫帚扫了几下

地，地上的尘土差点儿没飞进嘴里。放下扫帚后，他便宣布郊天之祭正式开始。

郊天之祭就是郊祭，从周朝开始便是一个国家最为隆重的祭典。郊祭结束以后，青铜台上的烤牛肉（也称作膰俎）会分发给文武百官，表示国家对他们的器重。

As soon as Lord Ji returned home, he eagerly asked the Rong Ji Dancing Girl to dance for him. As he was drinking while watching her dance accompanied with the melodious music, he became completely oblivious of everything else.

Dongye Bi entered and knelt before him, asking cautiously, "My Lord, should the roast beef be distributed to the civil and military officials?"

Lord Ji was enjoying himself very much, so he said "Yes, yes!" without even looking at Dongye Bi.

Suddenly he seemed to remember something and waved his hand, "Hold on!"

Dongye Bi stopped. He looked at Lord Ji, a bit perplexed.

The Rong Ji Dancing Girl sensed some anxiety in Lord Ji and asked, "What is it, my Lord?"

季氏大人刚到家，就迫不及待地命容玑舞女为他跳舞。在动听的音乐声中，他一边喝酒一边观赏乐舞，快乐得什么都忘记了。

东野毕走进来跪下，小心翼翼地问："大人，烤牛肉是不是应该分给文武百官了？"

季氏大人正喝得高兴，头也不回地说："发吧！发吧！"

忽然，他似乎想起了什么，挥挥手说："等等！"

东野毕站住了。他望着季氏大人，露出困惑的表情。

容玑舞女察觉到季氏大人心中烦恼，问道："大人，您怎么了？"

Lord Ji said,"There is one person that I am not sure if I should give him any meat."

The Rong Ji Dancing Girl moved closer and whispered to him,"Whoever makes the Lord unhappy should not receive any!"

Lord Ji's eyes lit up,"You are right!"

After Dongye Bi left Lord Ji's mansion, he quickly went to distribute the roast beef to all the officials in the State of Lu and didn't finish it until midnight. When he was just about to return home to rest, he was stopped by two people in the middle of the street. The horses were startled and the carriage nearly turned over. He was just about to unleash a torrent of curses at them when he recognized that the two were Zilu and Zigong.

Dongye Bi felt a bit guilty and asked nervously, "What do you want?"

Zigong replied,"Come with us, please."

季氏大人说："有个人，我不知道应不应该分给他。"

容玑舞女靠了过去，贴在季氏大人的耳边轻声说："谁让大人不痛快，就不分给他！"

季氏大人双眼一亮："有道理！"

东野毕离开季府后，快马加鞭地赶去向鲁国所有的官员分发烤牛肉，一直忙到了半夜。

当他正准备赶回家休息时，却被两个人当街拦住了，马受了惊吓，差点儿翻车。东野毕刚想大骂，忽然认出他们是子路与子贡。

东野毕有点儿心虚，哆嗦起来："你们想干什么？"

子贡说："请随我们来一趟。"

忠恕之道 **71**

Zigong and Zilu took Dongye Bi to the office of the Minister of Justice and asked him to kneel down. The students were standing on both sides of Confucius, their eyes all fixed on Dongye Bi, which made him feel really nervous.

Zilu asked angrily,"Are you the one responsible for distributing the roast beef?"

Dongye Bi stammered,"Ye.., yes, I have just finished."

"Then where is the portion for the Minister of Justice?"

Nangong stepped forward and asked.

Dongye Bi lowered his head,"Lord Ji ordered not to give any to the Lord Minister of Justice and the Duke agreed too."

Once they heard this, all the students started to shout,"Why? How can this be?"

　　子贡和子路把东野毕带到司寇府，让他跪下。学生们站在孔子的两侧，几十双眼睛齐刷刷地盯着他，让东野毕好不紧张。

　　子路生气地问："你不是负责分发烤牛肉吗？"

　　东野毕结结巴巴地说："是啊，我已经发完了。"

　　"那大司寇的呢？"南宫上前一步问道。

　　东野毕低下头说："季氏大人吩咐，不要分给大司寇，国君也同意了。"

　　此话一出，所有的学生纷纷嚷了起来："为什么？岂有此理！"

However, Confucius calmly told Dongye Bi to go home.

It was dead quiet in the hall apart from the sizzling sound from the burning torches.

Confucius said slowly, "Looks like it really is time I left."

Some students couldn't help but cry. Some who didn't cry out aloud were wiping their tears with their sleeves.

Suddenly there came the sound of footsteps. It was the elderly Qiguanshi helped in by Kong Li.

As Confucius and his wife looked at each other, his eyes also became reddened with sadness.

Qiguanshi said quietly, "Now that the State of Lu won't accept you, take them and go on to pursue your ideals."

孔子却平静地让东野毕回去了。

大堂上一片寂静，只有火把在"滋滋"燃烧。

孔子缓缓地说："如此看来，真的该走了。"

有几个学生忍不住哭了起来，还有的不敢哭出声，用衣袖悄悄地擦眼泪。

忽然，后边传来一阵脚步声，孔鲤搀扶着人到中年的亓官氏走了出来。

孔子和妻子对望，眼眶也有些红了。

亓官氏轻声说："既然鲁国容不下你，就带着他们去追求你的理想吧。"

Hearing this, his students all said one after another, "We shall follow the Master till we die. Wherever you go, Master, we shall follow you."

There was clear moonlight outside the window. Confucius' gaze moved to the window sill and saw the orchid that had accompanied him for so many years.

"Don't give up your ideals. This was what you told me and I shall never forget!" A bitter smile came on his face.

学生们一听，纷纷说："我们誓死追随先生！先生去哪儿，我们就去哪儿。"

窗外，是洁净的月光。孔子的目光移到窗台，看见了伴随自己多年的兰花。

"不要放弃自己的理想——这是你告诉我的，我永远不会忘记！"他的脸上泛起了一丝苦涩的微笑。

08

The Kuang People
● 《匡人》

The clouds in the sunset appeared to be like hazy red ribbons decorating the sky, one moment unfolded, the other moment scrolled up.

A few carriages and a line of people were travelling slowly through the woods. Ahead of them was a small city of the State of Zheng called Kuang situated on the border of three other states, Song, Lu and Wei.

Standing in a carriage, Confucius half closed his eyes and looked at the sunlight coming through the foliage. He couldn't remember how many days they had travelled, but he knew that they were getting farther and farther away from home.

One of his students Yan Ke pointed to the rundown walls of the City of Kuang and said, "Before I became your student, I was a soldier in the army of Yang Hu. We fought and attacked this city. Look, the crack over there was left by us and is still unrepaired even today."

While they were speaking, some students said they were tired. Confucius raised his hand and signalled everyone to have a rest.

夕阳下的云朵像晕红的丝带，时而舒展，时而皱卷，静静地点缀着天空。

几辆马车和一列步行的人徐徐穿过林间。他们的前方是宋、鲁、卫三国的交界之地——一个名叫匡邑的郑国小城。

孔子立在其中一辆马车上，眯起眼睛看穿过树叶缝隙的阳光。他已不记得走了多少日子，

但他知道，他们离家越来越远了。

学生中有个叫颜刻的指着破破烂烂的匡邑城墙说："跟随先生以前，我在阳虎的军队里当过兵。我们攻打过这座城，看那边的大口子，就是当时我们撞开的，竟然到现在还没封起来。"

说话间，有些学生喊累了，于是孔子抬起手，示意大家先休息一会儿。

Yan Ke continued to tell others about his story of coming to the City of Kuang in the past. He seemed to be really happy when he talked about his adolescent years, from how he joined the army to how the City of Kuang resisted their attack and to how he left Yang Hu's army. He just went on and on. Behind a big tree, there were another two pairs of ears listening to his

story. They carried firewood on their backs and it was obvious that they were from the City of Kuang, collecting firewood from outside the city.

The older one looked at the silhouette of Confucius and said quietly, "That man looked a bit familiar."

The younger one was his son who appeared a bit afraid, "They said that they had attacked us before."

　　颜刻继续和大家聊着过去来匡邑的事。回忆起自己年轻的时候，他仿佛很开心，一会儿说自己怎么参军的呀，一会儿说匡邑怎么顽强抵抗的呀，一会儿又说怎么离开阳虎军队的呀……说个没完。

　　在一棵大树的背后，正有四只耳朵竖起来在听。他们背着柴草，一看就是出城来砍柴的匡邑人。

　　其中年纪大的人盯着孔子的侧影，悄声说："那人看起来有点儿眼熟呀。"

　　年幼的那个人是年纪大的人的儿子，有些害怕："他们说以前攻打过咱们。"

The father raised his head and showed a scar on his forehead. "Now I remembered. That man is called Yang Hu. Ten years ago he led an army from the State of Jin that was passing our city, but they came in and killed many innocent people. Truly detestable!"

Their heart sank. They hurried back to the city along a hidden path.

When they told others that there were people from Lu outside the city, those who still remembered that bloody battle became very angry. They took up their farming tools and followed the father and son to the outside of the city.

The father who found the Lu people first pointed to Confucius and shouted, "Seize Yang Hu and take revenge for our people!"

His shout was as loud as thunder. Hearing this, the Kuang people charged towards Confucius and his students in a mass. Before they could react, Confucius and his students found themselves surrounded by the Kuang people.

"What do you want?" Zilu stood protectively in front of Confucius' carriage with his hand on his sword hilt.

父亲抬起头，露出额角的一道疤痕："我想起来了，那个人叫阳虎，十年前带着晋国的军队路过咱们匡邑，竟然跑进来滥杀无辜百姓，太可恨了！"

父子俩心中一凉，赶紧沿着隐秘的小路，跑进城里。

他们把鲁国人在城外的消息一说，还记得那场血战的匡邑人都愤怒了，纷纷抓起自己的农具，随他

们来到城墙外。

最先发现鲁国人的那位父亲指着孔子大喊："抓住阳虎，为民报仇！"

这呐喊如同一声惊雷。匡人听了，接二连三地迅速冲向孔子他们。孔子一行还没反应过来，就发现自己被匡人包围了。

"你们要干什么？"子路护住车上的孔子，一手按住剑。

"Yang Hu, you destroyed our families many years ago. Now it is time to pay you back!" One of the Kuang people shouted.

Zilu said anxiously,"You are mistaken. He is not Yang Hu. He is Master Confucius from the State of Lu."

"Rubbish!" Another Kuang man picked up a piece of clay and threw it at the carriage.

The other people all followed him and lumps of clay flew down like rainfall.

Seeing that there was no way to end this, Zilu pulled the reins and shouted commandingly, "Charge through!"

Their carriages dashed through the encirclement and drove toward the State of Wei.

"阳虎，过去你害得我们家破人亡，今天该还债了！"一个匡人说。

子路急得不得了："你们认错了。他不是阳虎，是鲁国的孔子先生！"

"胡说！"另一个匡人捡起一块土块儿朝马车砸去。

其他人立刻学起他来，土块像雨点一样飞来。

子路见没办法了，只好扯动缰绳，大声指挥道："冲出去！"

他们的马车硬生生地突破包围圈，朝着卫国的方向驶去。

Ahead of them was a narrow and dangerous path with cliffs on both sides. The carriages of Confucius and his students were running along this path, with the Kuang people chasing madly behind them.

The wheels of the carriage were rolling forward on the uneven path. It was such a bumpy ride that the people in the carriages felt as if all their internal organs would jump out. But with his hands tightly clutching the carriage, Confucius was extremely calm and steady.

"What is hard won't be ground so easily, nor can one call what is white black. They will definitely understand their mistake in the future." Confucius spoke to himself.

It was getting dark. As they were from Lu and didn't know the path well, they were a bit lost and finally found themselves in a dead end of the path in the woods. The Kuang people following them blocked their only way out.

Yan Ke really regretted what he had said and kept saying,"It is all my fault. I talked too much!"

前方是一条险峻、狭窄的山路，身旁就是陡峭的悬崖。孔子和学生们的马车沿着这条路不停地跑，匡人在后面拼命地追。

车轮在凹凸不平的地面上滚动，车厢里的人似乎连五脏六腑都要被颠出来了。孔子紧紧抓住车辕，心情竟异常平静。

"坚硬的东西磨不薄，洁白的东西染不黑。他们以后一定会

明白的。"他在心里告诉自己。

天渐渐暗下来。这群不熟悉道路的鲁国人越走越迷茫，最后迷失在一片林间绝地里，被紧紧跟随的匡人堵住了唯一的去路。

颜刻后悔得肠子都青了，一个幼儿说："都怪我多嘴！"

Zigong was very angry."We told them that the Master is not Yang Hu. Why didn't they believe us?"

With his Guqin in his arms, Confucius sat under a tree beside his carriage and said to his students,"We shouldn't blame the Kuang people for this. Their deep hatred is the result of Yang Hu's actions that once destroyed their homes and killed so many of their families."

Just then Zigong stood up and said, "Master, I think it is not far to the State of Wei from here. I am from Wei. Please let me try to break through them and seek help from Wei."

Confucius put his hand on Zigong's shoulder with a light squeeze,"Make sure to return safely!"

子贡很生气："跟他们说不是阳虎，怎么就是不信呢！"

孔子抱着自己的琴，坐在马车旁的树下，对学生们说："这不怪匡人。是阳虎曾经害得他们家破人亡，才积下了这么深的仇恨。"

这时，子贡站起来说："先生，这地方应该离卫国不远，而学生是卫国人，请让学生突围出去，到卫国寻求援助！"

孔子抓着他的肩，用力捏了捏："千万要平安回来！"

"Yes, Master!" Zigong jumped on a light carriage, and charged determinedly towards the part of the Kuang encirclement where there were relatively fewer people.

The Kuang people didn't expect this and hurried to move to avoid the carriage. Thus, Zigong successfully broke through their blockade.

It was a very dangerous night with the Kuang people shouting and torches burning around them like pursuing ghosts. It was also a difficult night as there was no news at all after several hours since Zigong had left. It was furthermore a tiring night as nobody dared to close their eyes. They clutched their weapons in their hands and ready to begin battles at any time.

　　"是！"子贡跳上一辆轻便的马车，盯准包围圈中人数比较少的地方，不顾一切地冲了过去。

　　匡人没有料到，急忙躲避。就这样，子贡成功地突围了。

　　这是危险的一夜，匡人的火把和叫喊如同幽灵一般久不散去；这是艰难的一夜，子贡已经离开了好几个时辰，仍毫无音讯；这是疲惫的一夜，所有人都不敢闭眼，手持兵器，随时准备迎接战斗。

When the dawn came and the birds started chirping in the woods, they finally saw Zigong and his carriage, followed by an army of Wei soldiers.

Confucius stood up, like a towering hill that couldn't be shaken. He said to his students, "Let's go now. This amount of hardship and misunderstanding are nothing to be concerned about. We have a long way ahead of us to go if we aim to pass on and revive the culture of rites and music."

当清晨来临，林中传来鸟鸣之声时，他们终于看到了子贡的马车，车后还跟着一队卫国士兵。

孔子站起来，如同一座屹立不倒的高山。他对学生们说："走吧，这点儿委屈和苦难不算什么。要传承、复兴礼乐文化，咱们的路还很长。"

Many a time, Confucius thought that one day he would go and visit the state where his ancestors came from - the State of Song.

That was over one thousand years ago. The royal family members of Yinshang who had been conferred the land arrived in the State of Song and became the local ruling aristocrats. A few hundred years later when there was unrest in the State of Song, some of the family members migrated to the State of Lu and ever since became mere commoners there.

The woods in the outskirts of the Song capital were thick with green foliage and full of flowers, as if they were welcoming home this wandering son who had been away for over a thousand years.

Confucius couldn't help but smile, for he was also a bit confused about whether he was then leaving his native place or returning to his hometown.

They took a rest under a big and old tree. Some were stretching their legs, some were sitting on the ground, while others were wiping their sweat off with their sleeves. Yan Ke stretched his arms and said,"It would be nice if we had some wine to drink!"

孔子曾无数次设想过，某一天要去看看自己的先祖之国——宋国。

那是一千多年以前的事了。受封的殷商王室成员来到宋国，成了诸侯；又过了好几百年，宋国动乱，家族中的一部分人迁到鲁国，从此变成了平民。

宋国国都郊区，树林郁郁葱葱，鲜花盛开，仿佛在迎接这个离家一千多年的"游子"。

孔子不禁一笑，有些分不清自己到底是背井离乡还是重归故里了。

他们在一株粗壮、古老的大树下歇息。有的活动腿脚，有的席地而坐，有的用衣袖擦去汗水。颜刻伸了一个懒腰，说："要是有口酒喝就好了！"

忠恕之道　**95**

Zilu was feeling bored, so he said immediately,"There is a ritual for drinking too. Let us listen to our Master speak about the protocol for drinking, shall we?"

They all looked toward Confucius who had just taken his Guqin out to play.Hearing this request, he nodded and said,"In the rural towns, the drinking ritual is like this: the host will welcome the guests from outside the house. Once the guests enter the house, both sides should bow to each other three times with

hands folded in front. After the guests sits down at the table, they should take a morsel of food, and then have a sip of wine to show their respect for the host…"

Zilu and Yan Hui started to play it out while listening to Confucius.

Suddenly there came the sound of horse hooves. After a short moment, a chariot appeared in front of them, followed by a few dozen soldiers holding axes. On the chariot was a man with a big beard who seemed to be their leader.

子路正觉得无聊，接口说："喝酒也是有礼的，咱们请先生讲讲喝酒的礼吧！"

大家把目光转向孔子。孔子刚把琴拿出来，准备抚上一曲，听见学生们的要求，便点点头，说："乡里饮酒的礼节是这样的，主人在门外迎接宾客，客人进门后，双方要作揖三次；客人入席后，尝一口食物，喝一口酒，表示对主人的尊重……"

子贡和颜回一边听，一边现学现演起来。

突然，远处传来一阵马蹄声。顷刻间，他们面前出现了一辆战车，后边跟着几十个手持斧头的士兵。战车上有个精壮的大胡子，看起来是领头的。

Zilu extended his arms to stop the chariot and asked, "Who are you?"

The big bearded man did not speak, instead a soldier replied, "How dare you speak like this! This is the Minister of War for the State of Song, Lord Huan Tui."

Hearing the name of Huan Tui, Confucius politely bowed to him, "How do you do! I am Confucius from the State of Lu."

The bearded man by the name of Huan Tui gave Confucius a slanted look, "I know who you are, Confucius! I am here especially to welcome you."

When Confucius and his students heard this, they couldn't help feeling a bit puzzled. How could someone welcome his guests in such an aggressive manner?

Huan Tui asked casually, "Confucius, your ancestors were from the State of Song. Now you have deserted the State of Lu and come back to the State of Song. Could it be that you want to become a citizen of Song again?"

子路展开双臂，拦在车前，高声问道："你们是谁？"

大胡子没说话，倒是一个小兵发话了："大胆！这是我们宋国司马桓魋大人。"

孔子听了桓魋的名号，客气地行了一个礼："你好，我叫孔子，从鲁国来。"

名叫桓魋的大胡子翻了个白眼："我知道你，孔子！我是专门

到这里迎接你的。"

孔子和学生们一听，忍不住犯起嘀咕：如此气势汹汹，有这样迎接客人的吗？

桓魋大咧咧地问："孔子，你先祖是宋国人，现在离开鲁国，跑回宋国，是不是想重新变成宋国人呀？"

Confucius felt this was a bit ridiculous. He shook his head,"I have never thought of that."

"Then do you think as a citizen of Lu, you can still become an official in the State of Song and supplant my position?"

Confucius shook his head again, "A gentleman unites in pursuit of morals, but doesn't collude. I have never had any intention to supplant anyone."

"If so, you shouldn't have come to the State of Song!" Huan

Tui sneered. He drew out his sword and pointed toward the tree,"Remove that tree!"

Two soldiers went forward and started to chop down the tree with their axes. It was a clear sunny day, but the big tree seemed to be in the middle of a storm, with its cones falling down one after another. Even the squirrels that were taking a rest in the tree tops raised their tails and fled quickly. The students standing under the tree also hurriedly scuttled back.

孔子觉得有些好笑，摇摇头："我从未这样想过。"

"那你以鲁国人的身份，难道还想在宋国做官，取代我的位置吗？"

孔子又摇摇头："君子周而不比，我更加没有想过替代任何人。"

"那你就别来宋国！"桓魋冷笑一声，拔出自己的宝剑，朝前面一指："把这棵树给我拔了！"

两个士兵走上前去，抡起斧头"咔咔"地砍了起来。在这晴朗的日子里，大树却像遭遇了狂风一般，果子不断往下掉，原本藏在树冠里休息的松鼠撑开蓬松的尾巴，灵巧地逃命去了，站在树下的学生们也纷纷倒退了几步。

Yan Ke said to Confucius quietly, "Master, let's get out of here now."

But Confucius stood firmly,"Don't be afraid! The Heaven above has entrusted me with the teaching of morals. What then can one Huan Tui do to me?!"

Crash! The tree that was as thick as a barrel fell and a giant gust of dust and broken leaves rose from the ground. From the rising mist a man appeared and he walked straight up to Confucius.

It was a young man of seventeen or eighteen years old, a bit chubby with an air of good natured honesty.

The young man said,"Master Confucius, I am Sima Niu. I would like you to advise me on how I can become a gentleman."

Confucius replied gently,"A gentleman has neither worry nor fear."

The young man scratched his head and wasn't sure whether he understood or not.

颜刻低声对孔子说："先生，咱们快点儿走吧。"

孔子站得稳稳的，说："别害怕！上天把德行交付于我，一个桓魋能把我怎么样？！"

随着一声巨响，水桶般粗壮的大树倒下了，地上腾起巨大的尘烟和碎叶。在那袅袅升起的烟雾中，

出现了一个人影，径直朝着孔子走来。

那是一个十七八岁的年轻人，长得胖乎乎、圆滚滚的，带着一股憨厚劲儿。

年轻人说："孔子先生，我叫司马牛。我想向您请教，怎样才能成为一个君子？"

孔子温和地回答："君子不会忧愁，不会恐惧。"

年轻人摸着脑袋，不知道有没有听明白。

At this moment, the voice of Huan Tui rang like a thunder, "Sima Niu? What are you doing here?"

Sima Niu turned around and cast him a glance, then said timidly, "Elder brother, Master Confucius is a very knowledgeable sage. Could you please let him stay?"

Huan Tui didn't expect that his usually docile younger brother would refute him. He became

really annoyed and raised an eye brow, "If you wish to help him, then don't call me your elder brother anymore."

Sima Niu clutched tightly the hem of his robe, warm tears filling his eyes. However he used all his strength to hold the tears back.

"I would like to be a real gentleman", he said to Huan Tui, "A gentleman who has neither worry nor fear."

　　这时，桓魋的声音轰然炸响："司马牛？你到这里来干什么？"

　　司马牛回头看了他一眼，怯怯地说："哥哥，孔子先生是学识渊博的圣贤，请你不要赶他走好吗？"

　　桓魋没想到平日里安分老实的弟弟会跟自己对着干，气得眉毛一竖："你要是帮着他，就永远别再叫我哥哥了！"

　　司马牛的手指紧紧缠住衣角，眼里泛起一些温热的液体，但他用尽自己的所有力气，没让泪水流下来。

　　"我想做一个真正的君子。"他对桓魋说，"一个不忧愁、不恐惧的君子。"

"Fine,"Huan Tui put back his sword, turned around and left."As long as you are not in the State of Song, I don't care even if you want to become an immortal."

Huan Tui and his soldiers went away. Confucius and his students also got on their carriage, ready to leave on a different road.

Life returned to the woods. The little animals that ran for their lives in fright came out one after another, playing games on the fallen tree.

Only Sima Niu remained where he was, speechless for a long while. In the distance as far he could see were the departing carriages of Confucius and his students.

"好！"桓魋收起剑，转身离去，"只要不是在宋国，你们去当神仙我也不在乎。"

桓魋的人马远去了，孔子和他的学生们也驾起马车，准备从另一条路离去。

林间又恢复了生机，方才还恐慌地逃生的小动物纷纷跑出来，爬到那棵倒在地上的大树上嬉戏。

司马牛独自留在原地，久久不说话。在他目光的尽头，是孔子师徒远去的马车。

10 The Eastern Gate

● 《东门》

The road stretched far into the horizon, and the State of Zheng's capital city Xinzheng came into view in the distance.

In the rocking carriage, Confucius was telling his students the story of Zichan, a virtuous and wise prime minister of the State of Zheng.

"Sandwiched between the States of Jin and Chu, the State of Zheng was small and weak. Almost every year it was rocked by unrest. It was only when they had Zichan that the State of Zheng gradually became strong and prosperous. His benevolence is the hallmark of the traditions of kindness and wisdom in ancient politics!"Talking of Zichan, Confucius became a slightly downcast,"Unfortunately, such a benevolent person is no longer with us."

His students all lowered their heads. They still  remembered clearly how four years ago when they were in the State of Wei their teacher wept with deep sorrow after he learned about Zichan's death even though the two had never met.

大道指向遥远的前方，郑国的都城新郑遥遥在望。

坐在颠簸的马车上，孔子给学生们讲起了郑国的贤相子产。

"郑国弱小，又夹在晋国和楚国之间，几乎年年不得安宁。自从有了子产，郑国才渐渐强盛起来。他的仁爱正是古代贤明政治的遗风啊！"说起子产，孔子有些伤感，"可惜如今这样的仁人已经不在

了。"

学生们低下了头。他们没有忘记四年前还在卫国时，先生听到子产去世的消息，竟为这个从未见过面的人悲痛得流下了眼泪。

Suddenly, there came from behind the unclear sound of people shouting and hurried footsteps. They turned around and saw a group of people were running with fright towards them with baskets on their backs as if they were being chased by ghosts.

"Old uncle, what is the matter?" Zilu stopped an old man and asked.

"Go inside the city quickly. The Jin army is coming!"The old man replied and immediately ran

for the gate of Xinzheng.

Zilu looked into the distance.

Sure enough, dust was churning in the horizon. He could see in the midst of the dust banners of Jin, the chariots and soldiers were rapidly moving towards them like a tidal wave. In response the Zheng army had also started to move in from the other side. It was clear that there would be a fierce battle between the two sides and the battlefield was where Confucius and his students were.

　　忽然，后边传来模糊的叫喊声和杂乱的脚步声。他们回过头，看见一小群百姓背着背篓惊慌地奔来，好似身后有鬼在追他们。

　　"大爷，出什么事了？"子路拦住一位老人问道。

　　"快点儿进城吧，晋国人打来了！"老人说完就赶紧朝着新郑的城门跑去。

　　子路抬头眺望远方。果然，地平线上扬起了漫天烟尘，"晋"字大旗忽隐忽现，快速行军的车马如浪潮一般涌来。而另一端，郑国军队也出动了。看来双方即将展开一场恶斗，而战场就是孔子一行所处的地方。

"Run now!" Zilu held his sword and shouted to his fellow students to leave the place. Some of the students panicked, looking left and right not knowing what to do.

"Don't panic!" Confucius said, "We will meet at the city gate of Xinzheng!"

The students then calmed down and with their belongings they ran towards the city gate separately.

In the chaos, Yan Hui held firmly the orchid that Confucius was so fond of and ran to the left. Suddenly a chariot charged out from behind him. Just as it was about to run into him, Yan Ke appeared from nowhere and pushed Yan Hui aside, but was himself caught in the waist by the chariot's axle shaft.

Confucius was in the carriage that Zilu was driving. When he saw this, he was stricken with concern. Throwing caution to the winds, he jumped off the carriage and ran towards them.

Chariots were rumbling past them and the dust stirred up engulfed everything. Under the scorching sun the battle started quickly yet came to an end swiftly.

"快跑！"子路提着剑，招呼所有的师兄弟赶紧离开大道。有些学生慌了神，左看右看，不知所措。

"别慌！"孔子招呼着，"咱们去新郑城门会合！"

学生们这才稳住神，各自带好行囊，分头奔向城门。

混乱中，颜回紧紧抱着先生钟爱的兰花朝左边跑。突

然，后头驶来一架战车，眼看就要撞上颜回了。颜刻不知从哪儿钻了出来，一把推开颜回，自己却被车辕擦伤了腰。

孔子原本在子路驾驶的马车上，看见这一幕后心急火燎，不顾一切地跳下车，朝着他们跑去。

战车呼啸而过，黄土飞扬，淹没了一切。烈日下，战争迅速展开，又匆忙结束了。

Most of the students had already entered the capital city of Zheng. In the open field, there were only the weak Yan Hui, wounded Yan Ke and grey haired Confucius who was already over sixty years of age.

"You stay here and look after Yan Ke," Confucius said. He found a piece of wood, tried it on the ground to make sure it could be used as a staff. "I shall go and look for Zilu and others."

"Please don't. You are wounded too," Yan Hui reached

out his hand, trying to hold Confucius back.

Confucius put a hand on Yan Hui's shoulder and said, "Remember, do not complain about fate at any times."

There was hardly any activity and life in the city of Xinzheng after the battle ended. Shops remained closed, and very few people in the streets. Even if there were the occasional passersby, they walked briskly along with their heads held low as if in a great hurry.

大部分学生都已进入郑国都城，荒野中只剩下赢弱的颜回、受伤的颜刻以及年过六十、头发花白的孔子。

"你留下照顾颜刻。"孔子找来一根木棍，往地上比了比，当拐杖长短刚好合适，"我去找子路他们。"

"那怎么行，您也受伤了！"颜回伸手想拉住孔子。

孔子按住了他的肩膀："记住，在任何时候，都不必抱怨命运。"

刚刚经历了一场战斗的新郑十分冷清。街道两边的店铺都关着门，行人也很稀少。偶有行人走过，也都是低着头，一副匆匆忙忙的样子。

Standing in front of a bean curd shop that was still closed, Zigong looked right and left and became increasingly worried."Master Confucius asked us to meet at the gate of the city, but Xinzheng has an Eastern, Southern, Western and Northern gate. Which one should we go to?"

Just then two people walked by while talking to each other.

One of them was very tall with a loud voice,"The stranger at the Eastern gate looked really weird. His forehead is like that of Tang Yao, his neck resembles that of Gao Yao and his shoulder looks like that of Zichan, but under his waistline, he must be three inches shorter than that of Xia Yu."

The short man nodded,"I wonder where they are from, but judging by their accent, they seem to have come from the State of Lu."

Hearing this, Zigong was overjoyed. He went up to them and said,"The man you are talking about is my teacher, a famous sage from the State of Lu."

子贡站在一家关着门的豆腐店门口，东张西望，心里十分发愁："先生说去城门会合，可是新郑有东门、南门、西门和北门，到底该去哪个门呀？"

这时，有两个人一边说话一边走了过来。

其中一位个子很高，声音也很洪亮："东门那个外乡人长得真怪，额头像唐尧，脖子像皋

陶，肩膀又像子产，可从腰部以下，却又比夏禹短了三寸。"

矮个子点着头说："也不知道是从哪里来的，听口音有点儿像鲁国人。"

子贡一听，心里乐开了花，迎上去说："你们说的这个人是我的先生，鲁国有名的贤人。"

The two men were startled by Zigong who had suddenly appeared from nowhere. But after hearing what he said, they showed with expressions of disbelief.

"A sage? He looked like an embarrassing spectacle." The tall guy said.

"He seems to me more like a stray cur." The short man continued.

"Rubbish!" Zigong's face darkened. He ran towards the Eastern Gate. He was quite unhappy with feelings changing between sadness and anger.

He finally reached the high Eastern Gate and could see in the distance a familiar figure in a dirty and ragged long robe, with grey hair, a high forehead and a pair of calm eyes filled with wisdom.

"Master!" He felt tears welling up and quickened his steps.

两个人被这个凭空冒出来的人吓了一跳，听了他的话又都露出不相信的表情。

高个子说："贤人？那人可是一副狼狈不堪的样子啊。"

矮个子接口道："我看倒像一条丧家犬。"

子贡脸色一变："胡说！"他朝着东门跑去，一会儿伤心，一会儿愤怒，心里非常不是滋味。

终于来到那高大的东城门，他遥遥地望见了那熟悉的身影：一袭肮脏破烂的长袍，花白的头发，高耸的额头，还有一双沉静睿智的眼睛。

"先生！"他鼻子一酸，加快脚步跑了过去。

Before he could get close, Zigong saw another scene which saddened him even more. Two Zheng soldiers carrying long pole arms on their shoulders and with a stern look on their faces came over, shouting,"Step aside, dont stand in the way!"They pushed people aside roughly and gave a hard push to Confucius as well when passing him.

The elderly Confucius staggered and only saved himself from falling over thanks to the support of the wooden stick in his hand.

Zigong rushed over to steady Confucius and said,"Master, how did you become like this?"

Confucius gave a sigh of relief when he saw Zigong,"You are all right? Thank goodness."

"The people here are really foolish. They even dare to jeer at you and say that you are like a stray cur."Zigong complained.

还没等他跑近，子贡又见到了更令他难过的一幕——两名扛着长戈的郑国士兵神色严肃地走来，口中连连叫嚷："闪开，别挡道！"他们粗暴地推开百姓们，顺手也用力推了一下孔子。

年迈的孔子一个趔趄，多亏

用手中的棍子在地上撑住，才没有跌倒。

子贡一把扶住孔子："先生，您怎么成这个样子了？"

孔子见是子贡，长舒了一口气："你没事吧？太好了。"

子贡埋怨道："这儿的人太愚蠢了，竟然嘲笑您像丧家犬！"

Confucius laughed heartedly, "I have heard that too. If they said I was a sage, well, that I may not be. But if they say I am a stray cur, well at least I currently look the part."

Soon Zilu, Ran Qiu and other students all arrived. Confucius told them about how Yan Ke was hurt and gave rough directions to where they were. Then they helped one another and went outside the city gate.

The sunset in the horizon was warm and beautiful. The moon also appeared from the other side of the sky as if it couldn't wait any longer. It took them some time before they finally found Yan Hui and Yan Ke. Then they continued with their journey towards the State of Chen.

The road continued to extend in front of them into far away distance.

孔子竟爽朗地笑了起来："我都听到了。说我像圣人，那未必；说我像丧家犬，我的模样正是这样啊！"

没过多久，子路、冉求，以及其他学生都找了过来。孔子说了颜刻受伤的事，又画出了大体方位，一行人便相互搀扶着出了城门。

前方的夕阳温暖而美丽，而高空的另一头，月亮已经迫不及待地出来了。他们花了不少时间，才找到了颜回与颜刻。然后，他们继续朝着陈国而去。

路，依然在延伸。

In the moonlight, the dark green vines were seen creeping in all directions, with long, thin and hairy gourds hanging on the vine. When the breeze came, the gourds would swing lightly from side to side like wind chimes.

Confucius stood in the courtyard and looked at the tiny white vine flowers with worry written all over his face.

This was a late night one year after they had arrived in the State of Chen. Zigong had just sent news that Duke Ding of Lu had passed away. What was worse was that the State of Wu was preparing to launch an attack on the State of Chen. They could no longer stay here.

It just so happened that some time ago, the Monarch of the State of Chu had sent an emissary to Confucius inviting him to Chu. Confucius looked at the gourds and thought to himself: I am getting old, but what value do I have to others if I am like these gourds just hanging there and be of no use to others? He finally made up his mind to leave this place.

月光下，墨绿色的瓜藤向四面八方攀爬，一只只细长翠绿、长满绒毛的匏瓜悬挂在藤上。风吹来的时候，它们轻微地摇动，就好像风铃一样。

孔子站在院子里，抬头看着细小、洁白的匏瓜花，脸上写满了担忧。

这是来到陈国一年以后的某个深夜，子贡刚刚传来消息，说

鲁定公去世了。更糟糕的是，现在吴国即将攻打陈国，孔子他们不能再留在这儿了。

恰好前段时间，楚国的国君派人前来邀请他。孔子看着那些匏瓜，心想：尽管我已经老了，但如果总是像这些匏瓜一样，挂在半空不让人食用，又有什么价值呢？他终于下决心要带学生们离开了。

The carriages swayed along in the open wild fields that bordered the State of Chen and the State of Cai.

Night came and they set up a camp and a campfire.

Zilu went out by himself to collect some berries. He suddenly stopped as he felt that there was someone behind him. He was about to turn round when a man cried out and held him from behind.

Without even thinking about it, Zilu got hold of the head of the person and threw him off.

Then a dozen of torches were lit. A group of strong and fiendish looking men bare to the waist were charging towards him.

Zilu was rushing back to the camp while shouting,"Robbers are coming!"

The students gathered themselves up,took up weapons and their belongings and carried Confucius running off. They ran until they came to a cliff. With the cliff in front and the robbers behind, they had no choice but to fight or die.

马车摇摇晃晃，行走在陈国与蔡国交界的野外。

夜幕降临了，他们燃起篝火，扎起营地。

子路独自来到营地外，想采摘一些果子。忽然，他警觉地停住了。他感觉身后似乎有什么人在跟踪自己，刚一回头，有个人就大叫一声，从后面抱住了他。

子路想也没想，反手抱起那人的头，将他扔了出去。

紧接着，数十个火把齐齐点燃，一群打着赤膊、凶神恶煞般的精壮汉子向他冲了过来。

子路一边朝着营地飞奔，一边大喊："有歹徒！"

学生们纷纷打起精神，拿起兵器和行囊，背上孔子跑到一处悬崖。现在，前面是绝路，后面是歹徒，唯一的办法就是背水一战。

However, a strange thing happened.

The robbers didn't advance to attack nor did they retreat. They just surrounded Confucius and his students under the cliff.

Confucius and his students were all puzzled, but the food they carried with them was diminishing day by day.

One day, two men came to inspect the situation underneath the cliff. They were dressed in luxury clothes and looked like senior government officials. The head of the robbers went up to them and asked humbly, "My Lords, we have surrounded them for a few days already. What is the next?"

"You don't need to do anything, just keep them penned in."One of them said. He was a senior official from the State of Chen.

The head of the robbers was surprised to hear this."Who are these people? Why should we keep them surrounded?"

然而，奇怪的事情发生了。

那群歹徒既不进攻，又不撤退，只是在悬崖底下围着他们。

孔子和学生们摸不着头脑，随身携带的粮食一天比一天减少。

这天，有两个衣着华贵、大夫模样的人来到悬崖底下查

看情况。领头的歹徒迎了上去，毕恭毕敬地问："大人，已经围困他们好几天了，现在该怎么办？"

"什么也不做，继续围困。"两人中的一个是陈国的大夫，他这样回答。

歹徒头子很惊讶："他们到底是什么人呀？咱们为什么要困住他们？"

The other one was a senior official from the State of Cai. He said, "Confucius and his students are going to the State of Chu. If King Zhao of Chu gives him an important post, it means trouble for both the States of Chen and Cai. However," He paused, "We could not afford to shoulder the burden of being the murderers of Confucius either. Therefore, keep them penned in like this for ten days to half a month, they will starve to death and that won't be our problem."

After saying this, they all chuckled.

The high cliff was exposed to the freezing cold wind from every direction. Confucius and his students sat in a circle around a big tree. Some of them had already fainted because of hunger and some had fallen ill.

Not very far from them was Yan Hui who was cooking. He found that there was only a handful of millet left. With a sigh he put the millet into the clay pot and added some extra water to make porridge.

　　另外一个是蔡国大夫，他说："孔子和他的学生要去楚国。一旦他被楚昭王重用，咱们陈蔡两国就有麻烦了。但是，"他停顿了一下，"杀死孔子的罪名我们又承担不起，所以就让你们这样围上个十天半个月。到时候他们活活饿死，可就和我们没什么关系了。"

　　说完，他们冷冷地笑了起来。

　　高高的悬崖上，寒风从四面八方吹来，大家围成一圈，坐在一棵大树下。学生们有的饿晕了，有的病倒了。

　　颜回在不远处做饭。他发现只剩下最后一小把米了，叹了一口气，把米放进陶锅里，多加了一些水，想要煮成米粥。

"Chirp, chirp," overhead came the sound of birds. Yan Hui looked up and saw two little birds extending their wings ready to fly. As their claws pushed back, some pieces of bark scratched by their claws fell onto the surface of the porridge.

"Oh," Yan Hui gave out a surprise cry and scooped up the dirty bit out with a small wooden ladle. He was about to throw it away when he suddenly remembered their situation and sighed. "It would be a waste to throw it away."

On saying that, he ate the bit of porridge that had broken bark in it.

Zigong, with firewood in his arms, was astonished to see this from not far away.

He walked briskly back to the tree and in time

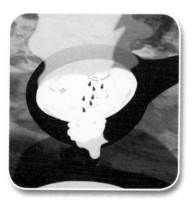

heard Zilu was asking Confucius, "Master, would a real gentleman have fallen into such a desperate situation as ours right now?"

"吱吱！"头顶上方传来鸟叫声，颜回抬头看见两只小鸟张开翅膀要飞。它们的小爪子一蹬，一些树皮碎屑扑簌簌地落进了锅里。

"哎呀！"颜回一声惊呼，忙拿起一把小木勺把被弄脏的部分舀了出来，刚准备倒掉，忽然想起现在的处境，不禁叹了口气："唉，倒了就太可惜了。"

说着，他吃掉了这一口掺了碎屑的粥。

不远处，抱着柴草的子贡看见了这一幕，非常惊讶。

他快步走到树下，正好听见子路在问孔子："先生，真正的君子会落到我们这样的地步吗？"

Confucius said calmly,"A gentleman maintains his integrity and accepts the hardships he must confront; but a non-gentleman would do what they will without restraint when faced with a similar situation."

Zigong couldn't help but questioned, "Will poverty change the integrity of a kind and honest person?"

Confucius replied, "If a person changes his integrity when in poverty, how can he be

considered a kind and honest person?"

Zigong continued with his question, "For people like Yan Hui, will poverty change him?"

"Of course not,"Confucius replied firmly.

Zigong shook his head and gave an account of how he saw Yan Hui sneakily eating porridge just now.

孔子平静地说："君子会安守穷困，而小人穷困时便会胡作非为。"

子贡忍不住问道："穷困会改变一个仁人廉士的气节吗？"

孔子回答："如果在穷困的时候就改变气节，那怎么还能算是仁人廉士呢？"

子贡接着问："像颜回这样的人，贫困不会改变他的气节吧？"

孔子十分肯定地说："当然不会。"

子贡摇摇头，将看到颜回偷吃粥的事说了一遍。

Just at that moment Yan Hui came back with the cooked porridge.

Confucius ran his hand through his beard and asked Yan Hui,"Yan Hui, can we use this porridge as an offering in a ceremony to our ancestors?"

Yan Hui immediately replied politely,"No, this porridge cannot be used as offering for ancestors. Because when I was cooking the porridge, some dirt fell in. As I didn't want to waste it, I scooped it out and ate it. To offer porridge that has been eaten to our ancestors would not be respectful."

Confucius smiled warmly and Zigong realized that he had wronged Yan Hui.

The following day, Zigong found a way to break through the encirclement and disappeared for a few days.

It was a very cold dawn, with a light mist lingering in the mountains. A few students were lying on the ground, too weak to stand up.

正在这时，颜回端着煮好的粥走来了。

孔子捋着胡须问颜回："颜回，这锅粥我们能拿去祭祀祖先吗？"

颜回听了，马上恭敬地对孔子说："这粥已经不能用来祭祀祖先了。因为刚才在煮粥的时候，有脏东西掉进去，学生不敢浪费，就舀出来吃了。用已经吃过的粥祭祀祖先，是不恭敬的啊！

孔子露出了欣慰的笑容。子贡这才知道自己误会颜回了。

第二天，子贡想办法突破包围冲了出去，连着几天几夜没有消息。

被困在悬崖上的人们迎来了一个寒冷的黎明，雾气淡淡地流动在山间。有几个学生躺在地上，连站起来的力气都没了。

Zilu said to everyone,"If Zigong is not back today, let's try and break through."

Right at that time, a large army came to them like a wave. It turned out that Zigong had asked for help from Lord Ye gong of Chu, who assembled his army and rushed over as fast as they could.

The robbers threw away their weapons and scattered. The two senior officials from the States of Chen and Cai also fled into the woods together to run for their lives.

Lord Yegong was in the same chariot with Zigong. When he saw Confucius, he hurried to get off the chariot and bowed to Confucius,"Sir, you have suffered so much. The King of Chu wanted to give you a high position. But unfortunately he died suddenly yesterday, so this matter will take more time. But I would like to invite you to stay for a while in my fief city."

Confucius nodded,"Many thanks!"

　　子路对大家说："如果今天子贡再不回来，我们就冲出去吧。"

　　正在这时，只见黑压压的大军像潮水般迅速涌来。原来子贡已向楚国大夫叶公求助，他们立刻集结部队，以最快的速度赶了过来。

　　歹徒们纷纷丢下武器，四散而逃。陈国与蔡国的那两个大夫也相互拉扯着，钻进树林逃命去了。

　　和子贡同车的叶公一见孔子，赶紧下车行礼："先生受苦了。原本楚王想重用先生，可惜国君昨日突然去世，这件事恐怕要耽搁了。但是，我想请您到我的封邑去住上一段日子。"

　　孔子点点头："多谢了！"

12

Fellow Students

● 《同门》

Confucius and his students stayed for many days at the fief city of Lord Yegong. On one cloudy afternoon, they finally bid farewell to Lord Yegong and continued their journey towards the State of Wei.

One person who had become Confucius's student recently was Gongliang Ru. He was tall and brave and was from an aristocratic family in the State of Chen. He abandoned his privileged and comfortable life, took his chariots and servants and followed Confucius on his wanderings from one state to another.

Yan Ke asked Gongliang Ru with a smile,"Master Confucius is not going to war but promoting the idea of benevolent governance. Why do you bring your soldiers and chariots with you?"

Gongliang Ru replied,"I did this for the sake of protecting Master Confucius in case we run into trouble."

Yan Ke shook his head and said,"If we run into trouble, we should try to negotiate first."

Gongliang Ru became agitated,"You coward! A brave warrior would never sue for peace with the enemy!"

孔子师徒来到叶公的封邑，住了好些日子。在一个阴天的下午，他们告别了叶公，朝着卫国而去。

有一个刚拜师不久的学生名叫公良孺，是陈国的贵公子，生得高大勇武。他放弃了舒适的生活，带上私家兵车和随从，跟随孔子颠沛流离，四处漂泊。

颜刻笑着问他："先生四处推行仁政，又不是去打仗，你为什么要带着兵车呢？"

公良孺说："我是为了保护先生啊，万一遇到麻烦呢？"

颜刻摇摇头："遇到麻烦，我们可以去谈判呀。"

公良孺着急了："你这个胆小鬼！勇士是不会向敌人求和的！"

"Who is a coward?!" Yan Ke was displeased too. So the two quarreled for a while and then turned their heads away in a huff and would not speak to each other again.

At that time, they were on their way to the capital of the State of Wei. They bypassed a small Wei city, the City of Puyi. The sky was covered with thick dark clouds and looked very gloomy, like a water colour painting full of ill omens. The peaks in front of them seemed as if they were trying to hide some dark and unfathomable secret.

Confucius looked up at the slopes on both sides of the road and felt unease in his heart.

Suddenly there came the sound of surprised shouting and whinnying of horses from the front. Some carriages and chariots trampled on the tree branches and fell into the big pits underneath.

"谁是胆小鬼？！"颜刻不高兴了。两人吵了几句，都把头一扭，谁也不答理谁了。

此时，他们的车队正驶往卫国国都，中间要经过一座偏僻的卫国小城——蒲邑。乌云密布的天空阴沉得好似一副杀气腾腾的水墨画，眼前的山峦仿佛隐藏着什么秘密。

孔子抬起头，看着左右两边夹道的山坡，心中生起一丝不祥的感觉。

突然前方传来惊叫和马嘶，有几辆马车踩断了树枝，落进了凹陷的大坑中。

"Traps!" They reacted immediately. The carriages behind turned around in a hurry and drove towards the sides of the road.

There was another pit and then another, almost all of the carriages and chariots had fallen into the traps.

A line of hunting dogs appeared, baring their white fangs. Their heavy panting was a sign that they were waiting impetuously for the signal to strike.

"Capture Confucius!" A man was shouting at the top of the hill. Over a hundred soldiers charged down the slopes. The students who had fallen into the traps didn't dare to tarry. They struggled out of the pits, helped Confucius up and ran towards another mountain.

It was difficult to navigate inside the dense woods and they couldn't find a way out. But their tracks were detected by the hunting dogs, so the soldiers chasing them quickly surrounded them.

"Gongsun Xu?" Confucius recognized that their leader was a senior official from the State of Wei where the two had met before. "Why do you waylay us?"

"是陷阱！"他们立刻就反应过来。后面的马车赶紧调转方向，朝两边驶去。

又一个大坑！又一个大坑！几乎所有的马车都没能逃脱。

一排猎犬探出脑袋，露出森森白牙，粗重的喘气声显露出它们迫不及待的心情。

"抓住孔子！"一个人在山顶上高喊，上百名士兵呐喊着冲下山来。落入陷阱的学生们不敢停留，急忙挣扎着站起来，扶起孔子往另一座山上跑去。

山林又密又乱，他们找不到出路，足迹又被猎犬嗅到，追兵将他们团团围住了。

"公孙戌？"孔子认出带头的那个人是卫国大夫公孙戌，两人曾经在卫国见过面，"你为何阻拦我们？"

Gongsun Xu said slowly, "Master Confucius, you are going to the capital of Wei, right?"

"Correct,"Confucius nodded.

"Have you heard any rumours about me on the way here?"

When they heard this question, Confucius'expression became cold and his students all had worried looks on their faces.

They all remembered the rumours they had heard in the last few days while travelling. After he was dismissed by Duke Ling of Wei, Gongsun Xu

forcibly occupied the City of Pu and was getting ready to stage a rebellion.

Looking at the expressions on their faces, Gongsun Xu guessed that the truth must have already been leaked out. So he laughed and said,"Master Confucius, I need talented people. Please stay and help me to take over the State of Wei, what do you think?"

　　公孙戍慢条斯理地说："孔子先生，你们是要去卫国国都，对吗？"

　　"没错。"孔子点点头。

　　"你们在来蒲邑的路上，听到什么关于我的传言了吗？"

　　听到这个问题，孔子神色一冷，学生们的脸色也都变了。

　　大家同时想起这些天在路上听到的一个传闻——公孙戍被卫灵公驱逐后，占据了蒲邑，准备发动叛乱。

　　公孙戍看了他们的表情，知道消息一定泄露了，于是哈哈一笑："孔子先生，我需要人才。请您留下助我公孙戍一臂之力，拿下卫国，如何？"

Confucius remained silent and did not answer.

Gongsun Xu understood what this meant. So he waved his hand and said,"Then it is you who have asked for this."

As soon as he said that, the hunting dogs pounced across like lightening. Gongliang Ru let the other students provide cover for Confucius to leave first, then he charged to the front with his sword in his hand and shouted,"Today I am in danger here with Master Confucius, but I shall fight till I die!"

Tree leaves fell and swirled around the woods. Gongliang Ru brandished his spear and fought off a pack of around eight hunting dogs. But his arms gradually started to become heavy, his footsteps became more and more sluggish. He could feel that he was slowly losing his strength.

Just then a burning torch was thrown across to him. With great effort Gongliang Ru caught the torch, turning around he saw to his surprise that it was from Yan Ke.

"Use the torch fire to attack the dogs!" Yan Ke told him.

孔子沉默着，没说话。

公孙戍心里明白了，向后一招手："那就别怪我不客气了！"

话音刚落，猎狗们就像闪电般扑了过来。公良孺让大伙先掩护先生离去，提着剑冲到最前面，大喝一声："今天与先生蒙难于此，我宁可力战而死！"

树林里落叶纷飞，公良孺挥动长戈，同时与七八条猎犬搏斗。他的手臂开始变得沉重，步伐越来越艰难。他感到自己正在逐渐丧失力气。

就在这时，一支熊熊燃烧的火把从空中抛了过来。公良孺伸手接住，回头一看，竟然是颜刻来了。

"用火攻击猎犬！"颜刻提醒他。

Gongliang Ru immediately remembered that animals were afraid of fire, so he brandished the torch. The hunting dogs all backed off and dared not to move closer to him again.

The only cart left was abandoned beside him. Gongliang Ru suddenly had an idea. He swung his arm and threw his torch onto the cart, setting the sacks in the cart on fire instantly.

"Get on!" Following his shout both Yan Ke and he leapt onto the burning cart, gripping the reins and charging headlong towards the enemy.

The sparks of fire flew and the thick clouds of smoke rose. The soldiers from the City of Pu were struck with fear and wouldn't move to attack no matter what was said to them. Gongsun Xu was furious. He took up an arrow, smeared it with poison, then arched his bow and shot it at Gongliang Ru.

"Look out!" Yan Ke dropped the reins in his hand and threw himself towards the arrow, using his body to protect Gongliang Ru. Immediately after, the venomous arrow hit Yan Ke in his chest.

公良孺立即想起，动物都是怕火的，于是赶紧挥动手中的火把。猎犬纷纷退后，不敢再靠前了。

旁边停着仅剩的一辆马车，公良孺灵机一动，抡起胳膊将火把扔了过去。马车箱里的麻袋顿时被点燃了。

"上车！"随着公良孺一声叫喊，颜刻与他跳上火焰中的马车，拉起缰绳冲向敌人。

火星飞来，浓烟滚滚，蒲邑的士兵们害怕了，说什么也不肯往前。公孙戌气得要命，拿起一支箭，擦上毒液，拉开大弓，对准公良孺射了出去。

"小心哪！"颜刻扔掉手里的缰绳，横身飞扑，把身体挡在公良孺面前。就在那一瞬间，毒箭扎进了颜刻的胸口。

"Yan Ke!" Gongliang Ru shouted in distress. He threw his long spear at the enemy with all his might. Then holding Yan Ke in one hand and the reins in the other, he drove his chariot away and quickly disappeared into the dense forest.

Not long afterward, Gongliang Ru caught up with others. With great sorrow they buried Yan Ke by the road side and then once again resumed their journey.

"颜刻！"公良孺痛苦地大喊起来，奋力把长戈投向敌人，一手抱着颜刻，一手拉缰驾车，消失在了密林中。

没过多久，公良孺追上了同伴。大家悲愤地将颜刻的尸体葬在路边，重新踏上了旅程。

13

Returning to Lu

●《归鲁》

It was a starless and moonless night. The silent wilderness was draped in darkness.

A troop of soldiers from the State of Lu doused their torches, breathed shallowly, then ran behind a chariot and soon came upon a huge military camp. Not far from them was a trench filled with dry grass, and behind it were a wooden fence half the height of a man and rows upon rows of military tents.

Suddenly, a group of torch wielding soldiers wearing army uniforms from the State of Qi appeared from the tents. They threw the torches into the trench and almost immediately the camp was surrounded by a towering wall of raging fire. From behind this fiery wall came the sound of laughter and jeering,"All of you from the State of Lu are cowards!""People from Lu are useless!""As if they could defeat us people from the State of Qi!"

At that moment, one of the Lu commanders stepped forward. He drew his sword and shouted,"My teacher Confucius once said -One must be resolute when doing what is right! Now is the time to brave great danger and serve our state. Everyone, follow me!"

没有星星也没有月亮，寂静的旷野一片黯淡。

一队鲁国士兵灭掉火把，屏住呼吸，随着一辆战车跑向远方。没过多久，他们便来到了一座巨大的军营外。不远处的沟壑里装满了干草，后面是一排半人高的木栅栏和成排的军帐。

忽然，一群身穿戎装、举着火把的齐军从

军帐里现身，将火把投入沟壑，一瞬间，军营被熊熊燃烧的火墙包围，哄笑声和挑衅声从火墙后传来："鲁国人都是胆小鬼！""鲁国人不堪一击！""他们怎么可能打过我们齐国人！"……

这时，鲁国的一位将领走上前，拔出剑，高呼一声："我的老师孔子曾经说过——当仁不让于师！这是赴汤蹈火、为国立功的时候，大家跟我来！"

With that said, the commander charged towards the wall of fire. Following his lead, the soldiers from Lu raised their halberds and pole arms, leapt in the burning trench like moths to a flame. Their bodies were covered in fire, yet their bravery and determination could be clearly seen on their faces.

The Qi army panicked and one after another they turned tails and fled. The battle quickly ended with a victory for the army

of Lu.

A few days later, Lord Ji came to commend the soldiers. When he saw the commander that had encouraged everyone and led the charge at the crucial moment, he asked, "Ran Qiu, were you born with your great fighting abilities?"

Ran Qiu was no others but one of Confucius' favourite students. He bowed and replied, "All of my knowledge is learnt from my teacher."

　　说着，那位将领率先冲向了火墙。在他的带领下，鲁国士兵纷纷举着长铍、长戈，像飞蛾一般义无反顾地跳进了燃着大火的沟中。他们身上挂着火苗，脸上却带着勇气。

　　齐军慌了神，一个个掉头就跑。很快，战争以鲁国人的胜利结束了。

　　几天之后，季氏大人前来慰劳士兵。他问那位在关键时刻激励大家、领头突围的将领："冉求，你打仗的本领是天生的吗？"

　　冉求不是别人，正是孔子的得意门生之一。他鞠了一个躬，说："在下的所有学识都是跟在下的先生学的。"

Lord Ji immediately realized the person being referred to was Confucius who was currently a wanderer somewhere far away. This surprised him greatly, "Oh? Master Confucius even understands how battles are fought?"

Ran Qiu's voice was full of sincerity, "The school of Confucius covers learning both broad and deep. Military knowledge is but just one part! For the sake of the State of Lu, my Lord, please request Master Confucius to return!"

Lord Ji stroked his beard and thought for long time, "Just before my father passed away, he said to me that what he regretted the most was forcing the then Minister of Justice Confucius to leave. I believe I

should not repeat my father's mistakes." With that, he finally nodded, "I hear that Confucius is currently in the State of Wei. Ran Qiu, Fan Chi, the two of you go immediately and invite him to return!"

"Understood!" Ran Qiu and Fan Chi acknowledged happily.

Not long after, Confucius who had been away from the State of Lu for fourteen years finally began his journey home.

　　季氏大人立刻意识到他说的是在外漂泊的孔子，十分惊讶："哦？孔子先生连打仗都懂？"

　　冉求诚恳地说："孔门之学，博大精深，军旅只是其中一项。为了鲁国，请大人把在下的先生召回来吧！"

　　季氏大人摸着胡子，思考良久："我父亲去世时曾对我说，他最后悔的就是当初逼走了大司寇孔子，我想我不应该重蹈父亲的覆辙。"末了，他终于点点头："听说孔子现在在卫国。冉求、樊迟，你们速速去把他请回来！"

　　"是！"冉求和樊迟高高兴兴地抱拳答应。

　　不久之后，离开鲁国十四年的孔子终于踏上了归途。

After travelling for over a dozen of days and nights, their carriage arrived in front of the city gate of Qufu. Above the gate was a plaque upon which were written the two characters "Stone Gate".

The gate was gradually opened and there people had been long waiting for them. Zilu looked closely before recognizing them, "Kong Li, Ran Geng, Yan Lu, Gongye Chang... you have all aged!"

"Zilu, you look old yourself!" The group of old friends hugged each other tightly.

At that time, Yan Lu raised his head and saw approaching him was a white haired middle aged man with a haggard face. Yan Lu narrowed his eyes as he tried to recognize this person. After a long time he finally shouted out, "My son! Your...Your hair has turned white!"

Yan Hui hugged Yan Lu emotionally, tears falling onto his elderly father's shoulder.

Confucius calmly watched everyone, his snowy white beard blowing in the wind.

他们的马车走了十几个日夜后，来到了曲阜的城门前。只见城门上头悬挂着一个牌匾，写着"石门"二字。

城门徐徐打开，有人早就在那儿等候了。子路细细地辨认："孔鲤，冉耕，颜路，公冶长……你们都老了！"

"子路，瞧瞧你自己也一样啊！"这群老朋友紧紧地拥抱在了一起。

这时，颜路抬起头，看见一个头发花白、脸色憔悴的中年人朝自己走来。他眯着眼睛看了半天，忽然喊了起来："儿子！你……你头发都白了。"

颜回伤感地抱住颜路，眼泪扑簌簌地滴在老父亲的肩头。

孔子平静地看着大伙儿，雪白的长须在风中飞扬。

Just then, from within the crowd another middle aged man walked out. He suddenly knelt in front of Confucius. He wanted to say something but was cut off by his tears and sobs. After weeping for a while, he finally managed to speak, "Father, we finally meet again."

Confucius watch his son Kong Li, a sorrowful expression appeared upon his face,"I have been away for too long."

"Your son is not filial, I couldn't help mother to wait until your return." Kong Li said quietly.

Confucius was shocked. For a long moment he could not speak out a single word. His students noticed this and looked at him with concern.

这时，人群里走出另一位中年人，"扑通"一声跪在孔子跟前，几次想要说话，都被泪水和抽泣声打断了。几度哽咽之后，他终于开口了："父亲，儿子终于又见到您了。"

孔子看着自己的儿子孔鲤，脸上浮现出一丝苦涩："我离开得太久了。"

"儿子不孝，没能让母亲等到您回来。"孔鲤低声说。

孔子一愣，半晌没说出一句话来。学生们注意到了，都不无担忧地看着他。

After that brief moment, Confucius raised his head, looking towards the towering city gate and said, "What I am most grateful to your mother was her understanding and support at that time."He sighed deeply, his eyes once again full of strong determination,"Since we have returned, then let us begin anew."

片刻之后，孔子抬头望着那扇高高的城门说："我最感谢你母亲的，就是当初她的理解和支持。"他深深吸了一口气，眼中重新充满了坚定的力量："既然回来了，就让我们重新开始吧！"

14

A Debate about the Sun

●《辩日》

The lands of Lu were full of life in spring. The birds were singing and the swallows were chirping. The green grasslands were speckled with wild flowers. A young man was slowly guiding a carriage along the road. In the rocking carriage was Confucius who had then became a State Elder. As he watched the scenery of his homeland rolling by, a faint smile creped on his face.

"The world is so beautiful yet at the same time so mysterious!" Confucius said to the young man driving the carriage, "Zeng Shen, the knowledge that exists in the world is boundless. We must never be tired of learning, never stop in our efforts in exploring. One is never too old to learn."

Zeng Shen was a young man that had just become Confucius' student. At that moment he was deep in thought reflecting on what his teacher had just said. Suddenly he saw at a distance a strange object flying in the sky.

正值春天，鲁国大地生机勃勃，鸟儿啼，燕儿喃，翠绿的原野上盛开着星星点点的野花。有位年轻人赶着一辆马车缓步前进，微微颠簸的车厢里坐着已经成为国老的孔子。他注视着故乡的景色，脸上挂着浅浅的笑意。

"世界是多么美丽，又是多么深奥呀！"孔子对赶车的年轻人说，"曾参，世界上的知识无穷无尽，我们应该孜孜不倦、永不停息地去探索。活到老，学到老。"

曾参是个刚刚拜孔子为师的年轻人。他偏着头思考先生的话，忽然看见远处的天空有一样奇怪的东西在飞行。

It looked like a large multi coloured swallow, but it was flat. It was floating upon the wind, one moment to the east and another moment to the west, one moment high and another moment low. Yet most of the time it was merely steadily hovering in the air. What was

most striking was a long string tied to its body.

"Master, what is that?"Zeng Shen pointed at the object.

Confucius' eyes followed

the string from the body of the object downwards. He saw two children around the age of five or six were holding the other end. They were standing underneath a tree and laughing excitedly.

Zeng Shen stopped the carriage next to the children and out of curiosity asked,"Excuse me, but what is that you are holding?"

它看上去像一只体形略大的彩色燕子，但又扁扁的；它乘着春风在天上飘荡，忽而向东，忽而向西，一会儿高，一会儿低，但大部分时候，它只是稳稳地停在空中。更奇特的是，它身上还绑着一条长长的细绳。

"先生，那是什么东西呀？"曾参指给孔子看。

孔子的目光顺着细绳往下移。他看见两个五六岁的孩童抓着细绳的另一端，站在一棵树下嘻嘻哈哈笑个不停。

曾参将马车停在这两个孩子身边，好奇地问："请问你们手里拿的是什么东西呀？"

其中一个小孩说："这个叫做绢鸢，你们不知道吗？"

One of the children replied,"This is a kite, don't you know?"

The other child asked,"Old grandfather, who are you?"

Zeng Shen proudly replied, "This is no other than the famous venerable State Elder of the State of Lu."

"You mean the venerable State Elder who is said to know about everything?" The two children looked at each other then smiled, "If that is the case, how could he not even know what a kite is? Ha ha-ha."

Confucius also laughed and did not feel in the least insulted, but Zeng Shen blushed a bit with embarrassment.

With hands on his hips the child that had spoken first asked,"Then I would like to ask the venerable State Elder, is the Sun closer to us during the morning or at noon?"

When Zeng Shen heard this, he was stumped. He quickly turned around and looked to Confucius. He found that his teacher was shaking his head, indicating that he did not know either.

Shaking his braids, the second child said,"It is obviously the morning."

另一个小孩说："老爷爷，您是谁呀？"

曾参骄傲地回答："这可是鲁国鼎鼎大名的国老爷爷哦。"

"就是那个据说什么都懂的国老爷爷？"两个小孩你看我，我看你，咯咯地笑了，"那怎么连绢鸢都不知道呢？哈哈哈。"

孔子也跟着笑起来，一点儿都不觉得被冒犯了，倒是曾参，脸微微有些发红。

第一个小孩叉起腰："那我来问问国老爷爷，您说太阳是早晨离我们近，还是中午离我们近？"

曾参一听，愣住了，赶紧回头去看孔子，发现先生也摇着头，表示不知道。

第二个小孩晃着头上的小辫子说："明摆着早晨近。"

Confucius asked, "And why is that?"

The child replied, "The Sun at dawn is the size of a carriage canopy top, but at noon it becomes the size of a plate. Of course it is larger when it is closer."

The first child quickly cut in, "Wrong! The Sun in the morning is cool, yet by noon it becomes scorching. Isn't it closer when it is hotter?"

Hearing that, Confucius stroked his beard and said, "It seems what you both said sounds reasonable."

Unexpectedly the two children became unhappy, saying, "Only one of us should be right, which one is it?"

Confucius was at a loss and was unable to come up with a response.

孔子问："为什么呢？"

小孩回答："太阳刚出来时像车盖一样大，到中午则像个盘子，当然是大的时候近啊。"

第一个小孩赶紧往前抢了一步："不对！早晨的太阳是凉的，中午的太阳则烫人，难道不是热的时候近吗？"

孔子听了，摸着胡子说："你们说的好像都有道理啊。"

没想到他们两个不乐意了，说："我们俩只能有一个是对的，到底谁对？"

孔子没辙了，半天说不出话来。

Finally, one of the children sighed, "Never imagined the extent of the knowledge of the venerable State Elder is just like this."

After saying that, they passed the kite string to Zeng Shen and skipped away.

Looking at the back of those two innocent departing figures, Zeng Shen shook his head, "Master, don't listen to what those two kids said."

Confucius laughed, "Didn't I just say it? Knowledge is boundless, even at an old age there is always something to learn."

Zeng Shen couldn't help but laugh as well, nodding, "Your student now understands!"

末了，其中一个小孩叹气道："没想到大名鼎鼎的国老爷爷学问也不过如此嘛！"

然后他们把手中的绢鸢送给曾参，就蹦蹦跳跳地走了。

望着那两个天真的背影，曾参摇摇头道："先生，你别听那两个小家伙的。"

孔子大笑起来："刚才不是跟你说了吗？知识是没有穷尽的，要活到老，学到老。"

曾参也忍不住笑起来，点点头："学生明白了！"

15 The Death of Yan Hui
●《回逝》

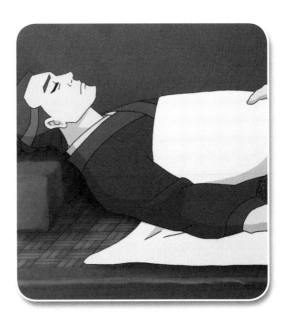

After returning to the State of Lu, with the help of Yan Hui Confucius focused solely upon his research, editing poems and books and writing the'Spring and Autumn'. Almost without notice four years had then passed.

Behind the lively market place of Qufu was a narrow alleyway. A long row of straw thatched houses haphazardly lined on both sides of the alley as it twisted and turned. The most Spartan amongst them was Yan Hui's home.

Zigong drove his carriage and carefully navigated its way through the alley. Many a time it nearly ran into the water vats that were placed next to the doors of the houses. Finally the carriage stopped outside Yan Hui's house.

Zigong raised his head and looked at the house: The roof was mud thatched and had wild grass growing out from it, the wooden doorframe had sections missing, the window was gone and three old clay pots were placed in the gap to keep out the elements.

孔子返回鲁国后，在颜回的帮助下，潜心钻研学问，修订诗书，写作《春秋》，不知不觉已近四年。

在热闹的曲阜市集后面，有一条偏僻的小巷，一长排灰扑扑的茅草屋参差不齐、歪歪扭扭地挤在巷子两侧。其中最为简陋的那个茅草屋就是颜回的家。

子贡的马车小心翼翼地穿行在这条小巷中，好几次差点儿撞翻放在门口的水缸，最后终于停在了颜回的家门口。

子贡抬头打量这屋子：泥巴糊的屋顶长出丛丛野草，木质的门框残缺不全，窗户是空空的，用三个破陶瓮摞起来勉强挡风。

忠恕之道　**179**

"Yan Hui!" He shouted.

A white haired thin man came out, holding a bamboo scroll. He raised his head and smiled,"Zigong, you came to see me?"

Zigong directed his servants to pass a sack of millet to Yan Hui,"Master Confucius wanted me to bring you some stuff. This is your grain supply for the month."

Yan Hui put the bamboo

scroll under his arm and took the millet. His expression remained unchanged from his earlier smile, "Sorry to have troubled you to come all this way."

"Yan Hui..."Zigong hesitated, "How about I help fix up your house? How can anyone live in it when it is like this?"

Yan Hui raised his hand to cut Zigong off,"Thank you for your kindness. However with a place like this to study, I am more than satisfied."

"颜回！"他喊了一声。

一个头发花白、身体瘦弱的人拿着一册竹简从门里走了出来。他抬起头，笑笑："子贡，你来找我？"

子贡指示家仆提起一袋黍米递给颜回："先生让我给你捎点儿东西，作为你这个月的粮饷。"

颜回把竹简夹到腋下，接过黍米，笑容依旧是淡淡的："劳烦你跑一趟了。"

"颜回……"子贡犹豫着说，"要不我帮你把屋子修一修吧？这样怎么住人呢？"

颜回抬起手，打断了子贡："多谢你的好意。但能有这样一个读书的地方，我已经很知足了。"

Zigong said no more, after bowing he left in his carriage.

Yan Hui turned around and went inside the house. Sitting down in front of his desk he looked at an opened bamboo scroll and continued his writing from where he left off. After writing for a while he suddenly crouched over the desk coughing violently.

Yan Lu hobbled over, patting his son on his back, "My son, are you all right?"

Yan Hui pointed weakly to the water vat, "Father, I would like a drink of water."

Yan Lu had just brought him some water when their thin door was suddenly pushed open and three young men appeared at the doorway.

"Zeng Shen, Ziyou, Zixia!" Yan Hui cried out happily as he saw it was his younger fellow students.

Zeng Shen quickly ran over, "Yan Hui, Ziyou and Zixia were discussing about the concept of the gentleman. Everyone's view points were slightly different."

子贡不再多说，行了一个礼，驾车离去了。

颜回转身走进屋里，坐到自己的几案前，对照着一份摊开的竹简继续写字。刚写了一半，他突然伏在案上，猛烈地咳嗽起来。

颜路颤颤巍巍地走过来，拍着儿子的后背

问："孩子，你还好吧？"

颜回虚弱地指指水缸："父亲，我想喝口水。"

颜路刚为他取来水，忽然薄薄的门板被推开了，门口出现了三个年轻人。

"曾参，子游，子夏！"颜回一见是自己的师弟，开心地喊了出来。

曾参三两步跑了过来："颜回，子游和子夏今天在谈论君子，大家的观点不太一样。"

Yan Hui nodded and then asked,"What did you say on this?"

Zeng Shen replied,"Zixia reckons, being a gentleman one should start from trivial things such as cleaning and sweeping…"

Upon hearing this Ziyou folded his arms and turned to face away in contempt.

Zeng Shen continued,"Ziyou on the other hand reckons that a gentleman should not be lost in the details of such trivial matters, but instead must focus on the bigger picture."

Zixia heard this and also turned to face another direction in a huff.

Yan Hui couldn't resist smiling, "Actually neither of you was wrong. There are many ways to become a gentleman. You should learn the good points from each other. For in the end it is through your own actions that you will prove what you are."

　　"你们怎么说的？"颜回点点头，问道。

　　曾参说："子夏认为，君子要从洒水扫地这样的小事做起……"

　　听到这里，子游抱着胳膊，不屑地转向一边。

　　曾参继续说："子游却认为，君子不应当被琐事困扰，要关心大事。"

　　子夏听了，也没好气地扭向另一边。

　　颜回忍不住笑道："其实你们俩都没有错。成为君子有很多途径，应该多学习对方的长处。最终证明自己的，是你们的行为。"

Hearing this, realisation instantly dawned upon Zeng Shen, Ziyou and Zixia. They happily bowed, "Thank you, Yan Hui."

They were just about to leave when all of a sudden Yan Hui started to cough violently and blood sprayed over the bamboo scroll like rain. Right after that, he passed out.

Zeng Shen and his fellow students were all frightened. Two of them stayed on to look after Yan Hui, and one ran to notify Confucius.

When Confucius came it was already late in the evening. The oil lamp cast a weak light in the gloomy room. Yan Hui was lying upon the bed, with his eyes closed, his hand still clutching that blood splattered bamboo scroll.

"Son, Master Confucius is here to see you." Yan Lu stroked his son's forehead as he spoke.

曾参、子游、子夏听了，茅塞顿开，高兴地行了一个礼："谢谢你，颜回。"

他们正准备离去，突然颜回剧烈地咳嗽起来，鲜血像雨点一样喷在了竹简上。接着，他晕了过去。

曾参他们吓坏了，留下两人照顾，另一人跑去通知孔子。

孔子来时已是傍晚。油灯微弱，房屋黯淡。颜回攥着那卷沾血的竹简，躺在床榻上闭目休息。

"孩子，先生来看你了。"颜路摸着儿子的额头呼唤。

Yan Hui opened his eyes and saw Confucius leaning on a staff, watching him with eyes full of concern.

He tried to put Confucius at ease, "There is no need to worry about me, Master. You are in the middle of writing the 'Spring and Autumn', which will record all the history of Lu and the world. This is a thing of great importance especially to people in the time to come. I, your student must help you."

"But you must look after your

health more." Confucius' reply was almost choked with sobs.

A few days later, Yan Hui's illness suddenly became worse. On a cold morning, he finally passed away. When Confucius rushed over, Yan Hui's body was already cold and covered with a white cloth. His complexion was sombre yet serene.

　　颜回一睁眼，就看到白发苍苍的孔子拄着拐杖，心疼地看着自己。

　　他反而安慰起孔子来："先生，别担心我。您在作《春秋》，记载鲁国和天下的历史，这是一件造福后人的大事，学生必须帮助您。"

　　"还是要多多保重身体啊。"孔子几乎是哽咽着说。

　　没过几天，颜回的病情突然恶化。他于一个寒冷的清晨死去。孔子赶到的时候，颜回的身体已经被盖上白布，肌肤冰冷，神情安详而沉静。

"Lord of the Heavens, you're taking my life!" Confucius' legs wobbled and fell next to the death bed, "Yan Hui lived in such a rundown alley, always trying his hardest to study. Every day he would be satisfied with just one bowl of rice and one ladle of water. How such a wonderful child could be taken away from us just like this!"

The graveyard at the outskirts of the city was desolate. In front of a small burial mound, a crowd of dignified looking people gathered.

A grand and expensive carriage approached slowly. Confucius stepped out from the crowd and bowed with both hands folded, "Your Grace."

The person on the carriage was Duke Ai of Lu, he nodded, "I have heard that you State Elder has lost a student. I have come especially to see you all."

"老天爷，你这是要我的命啊！"孔子腿一软，跌倒在灵床边上，"颜回住在陋巷，刻苦治学，每天一箪饭、一瓢水就能满足，这么好的孩子怎么就走了啊！"

郊外的墓地一片萧瑟，小小的坟堆前，围满了神色凝重

的人。

一辆装饰华贵的马车缓缓驶来。孔子从人群中走出来，双手行礼："国君。"

车上的人是鲁哀公，他点点头说："听说国老失去了一名学生，我特意来看看。"

With his red eyes from tears Confucius said, "Many thanks, Your Grace. This very student of mine was called Yan Hui. He never lost his temper at anyone and never made the same mistake twice. Yet he had the great misfortune to have passed away at such a young age." Raising his head and gazing into the grey skies, he said,"And now, there is no one with such a devotion to learning."

孔子双眼通红地说："谢谢国君。我这个学生叫颜回，他从不把脾气发到别人的身上，也不重犯同样的错误。不幸年纪轻轻就死了。"他仰起头，看向灰暗的天空："现在，再也没有这么好学的人了啊。"

16 Lasting Fragrance
● 《馨香》

Dawn had just arrived, and the morning fog slowly began to disperse. On the desk there was a pale blue oil lamp and a heavy bamboo scroll, they companied the person in front of the desk through the whole night.

Carrying a kettle of water, Zeng Shen carefully entered the room. There he saw the white haired Confucius was still writing with a brush pen. He couldn't help but speak with a concerned tone, "Master, it is already morning, please take a rest."

Confucius did not even raise his head, slowly speaking,"This 'Spring and Autumn' book is still not finished, yet my time is running out."

"Understood! "Zeng Shen bowed his head and refilled Confucius' tea cup.

Suddenly from outside the house came the sound of running footsteps and two people ran in, breathing heavily they said, "The Duke has just returned from hunting and has caught a strange animal."

天刚破晓，晨雾弥散。几案上有一盏青荧的油灯、一叠沉重的竹简，陪伴案前的人度过了整夜。

曾参提着一壶水，小心翼翼地走进来。他看见满头花白的孔子提着笔正在书写，不禁心疼地说了声："先生，天亮了，休息一会儿吧。"

孔子头也没抬，缓缓地说：

"这部《春秋》还没完成，而我的时间已不多了。"

"是！"曾参垂下头，给孔子的茶杯里倒满了水。

忽然，屋外传来一阵急促的脚步声，有两个人跑了进来，喘着粗气说："国君狩猎回来，捉到一只怪兽。"

Unable to control his curiosity Zeng Shen asked, "What strange animal?"

"I heard that it has the body of a deer, tail of a cow, hooves of a horse and on its head there is a flesh horn..." Head tilted, the other person thought for quite a while, "Hum. Right. It is said to be called Qilin."

Clack!

The brush pen fell down to the ground from Confucius' hand. He stood up unsteadily and asked, "Qilin?"

"Yes. After seeing it, both the Duke and Lord Ji feared it and they are going to kill it." The two new comers continued to talk without noticing that Confucius' expression changed abruptly. The light disappeared from his eyes and his jaw shuddered.

"什么怪兽？"曾参忍不住问道。

"听说长着鹿的身子、牛的尾巴、马的四蹄，头上还有一支肉角……"另一个人歪着脑袋想了半天，"对了，好像说是叫麒麟。"

啪嗒！

孔子手中的笔落到了地上。他颤巍巍地站起来问："麒麟？"

"是啊，国君和季氏大人见了害怕，准备处死它呢。"来人继续说，没注意到孔子神色大变，双眼失去光泽，下巴不住地抖动。

"Qilin is a benevolent beast. It cannot be treated that way." Confucius gave out a sigh while he supported himself and headed towards the door. He did not even notice when he stepped on the bamboo scroll that had fallen onto the floor.

"Master, this is your life's work!" Zeng Shen hurriedly knelt and picked up the yet to be completed 'Spring and Autumn'. When he raised his head, Confucius had already disappeared outside the door.

After about two hours, Confucius was helped back to his home by his students.

He looked even more haggard than before. He sobbed,"I had hoped to plead with the Duke to release that benevolent beast, but they still killed it. Qilin, you benevolent creature! Why have you come to this place?!" With that Confucius became silent and withdrawn for a long time.

Zeng Shen silently waited at Confucius' side, not daring to speak.

It was not until the dusk that Confucius finally spoke,"Help me go outside for a walk."

"麒麟是仁兽啊，不能那样对待。"孔子一边叹息，一边用手支撑着站起来，朝门口走去，就连竹简哗啦啦地落到地上、被他踩到也没注意。

"先生，这是您的心血呀！"曾参急忙蹲下去，将还未完成的《春秋》捡了起来。他一抬头，孔子已消失在门外。

一个时辰以后，孔子在学生们的搀扶下，返回了住所。

他看上去更憔悴了，哽咽着说："我本想请求国君放了仁兽，可他们竟将它杀了。仁兽麒麟，你为什么要来呀！"说罢，孔子便陷入了长时间的沉默。

曾参一直在旁默默服侍，不敢说话。

直到傍晚，孔子才重新开口道："带我出去走一走吧。"

Zeng Shen nodded and prepared the carriage. He then took Confucius to Ni Hill.

The evening wind was cool during the beautiful sunset. Confucius stood motionless and gazed at the small path at the foot of the hill as if waiting for someone.

"Master, it is cold here and your health has not been good." Zeng Shen said worriedly as he held on to the reins,"Let's go back."

Confucius raised his hand signalling he wanted to wait for a

while longer.

Just before nightfall, they finally heard from a distance the clip clop sound of horse hooves. A carriage appeared at the end of the road. Confucius squinted before finally recognized that the person in the carriage was indeed the one he had been waiting for.

"Oh Zigong, have you not come back too late?" When the carriage was coming near, Confucius leaned upon his staff and stepped forward to meet him.

曾参点点头，套上车，载着孔子来到了尼山。

晚风清凉，夕阳美好，孔子一动不动地望着山下的小路，似乎在等待什么人。

"先生，这儿太冷。您的身体不好，"曾参握着缰绳，有些不安，"回去吧。"

孔子抬起手，示意再待一会儿。

夜幕降临前，他们终于听到远方传来踢踢踏踏的声音，一辆马车出现在小路的尽头。孔子眯起眼睛，依稀辨认出站在车上的正是他在等的人。

"子贡啊，你回来得太晚了吧？"等马车走近，孔子拄着拐杖迎上前去。

Zigong hurriedly got off the carriage and helped his aging teacher,"Your student was on an errand. It was far and the journey was long. I am sorry to have worried you, Master."

"It is fine as long as you are back, as long as you are back." Confucius patted Zigong on his shoulder. Yet grief gripped his heart once more and he sang,"Will Mount Tai crumble? Will the pillar break? Is a Sage destined to suffer hardship?"

Seven days later, Confucius fell ill and became bed ridden. Crowded around him were his students and loved ones. As he gazed at the support beams upon his ceiling, his eyes instead seemed to have once again beheld that brilliant dawn over Mount Tai all those years ago. He could still hear that sound which reverberated throughout the valley,"I want to study!"

Outside the window, a bright shooting star flashed across the night sky before disappearing into the distance.

In the early hours of the ninth day of the fourth month during the sixteenth year of the reign of Duke Ai of Lu, the eyes of the great Sage Confucius closed forever.

子贡赶紧下车，扶住他年迈的老师："学生出使，路途遥远，让先生担心了。"

"回来就好，回来就好。"孔子拍拍他的肩膀，心里一阵感伤，不禁唱起歌来："难道泰山要崩坏吗？梁柱要折断吗？哲人注定要困顿吗？"

七天后，孔子病倒在床，四周聚满了学生和亲人。他望着天花板

上的横梁，眼中却仿佛看见了多年前那一轮泰山之巅的朝阳，还仿佛听见了那回荡在山谷里的声音："我要读书！"

窗外，一颗灿烂的流星划过夜空，消失在远方。

鲁哀公十六年四月己丑日的凌晨，圣人孔子永远地闭上了双眼。

Not long after that, a solemn yet respectably built tomb appeared at Sishui, which was about half a kilometre north of the capital of the State of Lu. Nearly ten paces long, thirteen paces across and four meters in height, it was the eternal resting place that Confucius' students built for their teacher. They also erected huts nearby and planted all kind of trees before settling in the huts to keep bereavement vigil for their teacher.

Three years later, on a glorious spring morning, Zigong emerged from his straw hut and gazed at the foliage in front of the tomb, lost in his own thoughts.

"Zigong!"someone called out to him.

Turning around he saw Ziyou, Zixia and some of the other even younger students approaching him with their bags packed.

Ziyou bowed and spoke first,"We have held vigil for our teacher for three years. It is time for us to leave, how about you?"

不久后，鲁国城北一里外的泗水之上，出现了一座端庄肃穆的墓冢，约十步长，十三步宽，一丈二尺高。这就是学生们为孔子修建的长眠之处。他们又在旁侧搭起了茅草屋，种上各种树，在茅草屋里住下，为先生守墓。

三年过去了，又是一个阳光明媚的春日，子贡从草屋里走出来，望着坟前郁郁葱葱的树木发呆。

"子贡！"有人在叫他。

他回头一看，只见子游、子夏和其他几名更年轻的学生背着行囊走来。

子游行了一个礼，率先说："咱们为先生服丧三年，该离去了，你呢？"

Zigong said sorrowfully,"I want to stay and keep our teacher company for another three years."

When they heard this, Ziyou and the rest felt their chest tightened and they nearly cried.

Zigong immediately said to them, "Go now. Make sure to pass on Master Confucius'teachings. Take care of yourselves!"

The fellow students sorrowfully hugged and bid each other farewell before departing their separate ways. Behind them was the dignified gaze of Zigong and that peaceful tomb.

Well then, at this moment in time, is the story of Confucius over?

No, the story of Confucius is far from over. Two thousand years have passed, yet Confucius' teaching and thoughts have been understood, accepted and taught by more and more people.

Right up to the present day, you could still hear people sometime saying "Confucius once said this" and "Confucius once said that" as they repeat his teachings. There are also people who worship him as a teacher to all the people in the world and still study that ancient but deep wisdom of Confucius.

子贡伤感地说："我想留下来，再陪先生三年。"

子游他们听了，心头一酸，几乎就要哭出来。

子贡赶紧对他们说："去吧，好好传播先生的学说，多保重！"

几个师兄弟伤心得不成样子，相互拥抱道别了一番后，诀别而去。在他们身后，是子贡凝重的目光和那座安详的墓冢。

那么，到这一刻，孔子的故事结束了吗？

不，孔子的故事远没结束。两千多年过去了，孔子的学说和思想被越来越多的人理解、接受、推崇。

直到今天，你时常还能听见有人在"子曰、子曰"地重复他的学说，还有人在祭拜这位天下所有人的老师，还在学习他那古老而深邃的智慧。

Inside the valley, the orchid that is termed the "Gentleman amongst the flowers" has bloomed. Its light fragrance is reaching far as it flies upon the gentle winds…

山谷里，被称为"花中君子"的兰花开了，淡雅的芬芳随着微风吹向了天际……

图书在版编目（CIP）数据

孔子卡通传记：英汉对照/深圳市崇德影视传媒有限公司编著.
—青岛：青岛出版社，2011.11
孔子学院教材系列
ISBN 978-7-5436-7526-1

Ⅰ.①孔…Ⅱ.①深…Ⅲ.①汉语–对外汉语教学–教材②动画：连环画–中国–现代
Ⅳ.①H195.4②J228.7

中国版本图书馆CIP数据核字（2011）第176813号

书　　　名：	孔子卡通传记 忠恕之道	
出　　　品：	深圳市崇德影视传媒有限公司	
	中国孔子基金会	
出 版 发 行：	青岛出版社	
本 社 网 址：	http://www.qdpub.com	
本 书 网 址：	http://www.kz928.com	
邮 购 电 话：	(0086)755-83516418　(0086)13724376536	
总 策 划：	许　琳　李　群	
总 顾 问：	季羡林 范　曾　韩喜凯	
	孙守刚　王京生	
出 品 人：	梁国典　孟鸣飞　赵先德	
策　　　划：	王大千　易　容	
总 导 演：	赵先德	
总 编 剧：	曹小卉　李　冯	
编　　　著：	赵先德　谭笑沨	
翻　　　译：	李明芳　张新生	
英 文 校 对：	赵小林	
美 术 设 计：	李　剑	
责 任 编 辑：	刘耀辉 电 话：（0086）532-68068787	
制　　　版：	利丰雅高印刷(深圳)有限公司	
印　　　刷：	利丰雅高印刷(深圳)有限公司	
出 版 日 期：	2011年11月第1版 2011年11月第1次印刷	
开　　　本：	16开（710mm×1000mm）	
总 印 张：	48.75	
总 字 数：	800千	
书　　　号：	ISBN 978-7-5436-7526-1	
定　　　价：	298.00元（全4册）	

编校质量、盗版监督服务电话　4006532017

（青岛版图书售后如发现印装质量问题，请寄回青岛出版社印刷物资处调换。

电话：（0086）532-68068629）

Cataloguing in Publication Data

Confucius Cartoon Biography: English and Chinese/Compiled by Shenzhen Cherid Film

Dissemination Co., Ltd

 — Qingdao: Qingdao Publishing House, November 2011

Confucius Institutes Teaching Material series

ISBN 978-7-5436-7526-1

I.①Confucius⋯ Ⅱ.①Shenzhen⋯ Ⅲ.①Chinese–Teaching Chinese as a Foreign Language–

Teaching Materials ②Animation: Picture Storybook–China–Modern⋯ Ⅳ.①H195.4②J228.7

Chinese Publications Number of Archives Library: 2011–176813

Title:	A Cartoon Biography of Confucius – Doctrine of Loyalty and Forgiveness
Produced by:	Shenzhen Cherid Film Dissemination Co., Ltd
	China Confucius Foundation
Published by:	Qingdao Publishing House
Publisher's website:	http://www.qdpub.com
Title's website:	http://www.kz928.com
Tel of Sales Department:	(0086)755–83516418 (0086)13724376536
Chief Planners:	Xu Lin, Li Qun
General advisors:	Ji Xianlin, Fan Zeng, Han Xikai,
	Sun Shougang,Wang Jingsheng
Produced by:	Liang Guodian, Meng Mingfei, Zhao Xiande
Planners:	Wang Daqian,Yi Rong
Chief Director:	Zhao Xiande
Chief Screenwriters:	Cao Xiaohui, Li Feng
Complied by:	Zhao Xiande, Tan Xiaofeng
Translated by:	Linda M Li, George X Zhang
English proofreader:	Zhao Xiaolin
Art design:	Li Jian
Editor:	Liu Yaohui Tel: (0086) 532–68068787
Plate set by:	Toppan Leefung Printing (Shenzhen) Co.,Ltd.
Printed by:	Toppan Leefung Printing (Shenzhen) Co.,Ltd.
Date of Publication:	First edition, first published in November 2011
Size:	1/16(710mm × 1000mm)
Total Printed Sheets:	48.75
Total No of Words:	800,000
ISBN:	978–7–5436–7526–1
Price:	￥ 298.00 (4 volumes)

Telephone number for reporting quality and piracy issues: 4006532017

(If there is any problem with printing or binding with the book after sales, please contact Printing

Materials Department of Qingdao Publishing House. Tel: （0086）532–68068629）